Rude Xmas Jokes

The Xmas Fairy

Rude Xmas Jokes

A copy of this publication can be found in the National Library of Australia.

ISBN: 978-1-921791-39-0 (pbk.)

Published by Book Pal
www.bookpal.com.au

Acknowledgements

The Xmas fairy invites you to enjoy this collection of jokes from the finest sources of life and the most elegant of establishments.

Most were heard in pubs, clubs, parties, backyard-barbeques and of course, let's not forget the walls of the bathroom facilities at the Faculty of Medicine Sydney University.

And a special thank you to all who contributed, Roy Pemberton, Suellen Spiteri, Sonny Rawlings, Warren Kermond, Janette Goodall, Steve Hodgson and Michael Weeks.

And an extra special thank you to Michele Walters.

Thanks again from the Xmas Fairy

Xmas Joke Book Characters

Santa Claus..........................His wife Mrs. Claus

Santa's father.....................................Old Timer

Rudolph....................................His wife Dancer

Santa's elves..................Stupid, Jack and Emerald
the Irish elf.

The Xmas Fairy..............Her love child Mary Xmas

Fairy Floss.....................Cousin to the Xmas Fairy

Ken Floss..........................Fairy Floss's Husband

Fairyboy..........................Fairy Floss & Ken's Son

Sister Slosh............................North Pole Church

The Sleaze family.........................Ima and Sucha

Trash......................................Ima & Sucha's son

Trashette....................................Their daughter

Polestar............................The North Pole singer

Desperate Doris................The Randy Senior-Cit.

Contents

Santa Jokes.

Xmas eve dawned and the elves were pissed. Santa packed the sleigh without help. He was fed up and went to have a good strong scotch, before delivering to the world.

But the elves had finished off the scotch, not a drop was left and now someone was rudely leaning on the doorbell.

Santa yanked the door open to find the Xmas Fairy, holding a decorated tree.

'Hi ya Fat Stuff,' she yelled, 'where the fuck do you want this tree?'

And that my friend is the story of how the fairy came to be on top of the Xmas tree.

***

'Santa, how would you blindfold an Asian?' Jack the elf asked.

'Hmmm, probably with a really thin piece of tinsel!'

***

'Michelle Obama has just filed for divorce against President Obama,' Santa informed the Xmas Fairy.

'I don't believe it, why would she divorce the President?'

'Because he's no longer doing to her - what he's doing to the country!'

***

'The Xmas Fairy is such a slut,' Rudolph said. 'Santa, how do I stop her from over indulging in sex?'

'That's easy,' said Santa.

'Marry her!'

***

The elderly lady approached Santa's sleigh. 'Santa, I wonder if you would give me a lift to the pet cemetery. The nasty bus driver won't allow me on the bus with my dead pussy.'

'Climb aboard,' said Santa, 'sit next to Mrs. Claus and you'll have another dead pussy for company.'

***

'Santa I read somewhere that women have 50% more brains than cows.'

'That figgers, you can pull a woman's tits and she won't shit on the floor!'

***

Santa's toy factory stood on a large portion of land. He decided to go into farming and plant a crop of dildos.

'Santa, will you make a lot of money out of dildos?' Rudolph asked.

'Not really, but they'll sure keep the squatters away!'

***

Santa and Polestar the North Pole singer met at Monaco. Santa was carrying a large package.

'What that?' Polestar asked.

'I got a top of the range fishing rod for Mrs. Claus.'

'Holy shit Santa.

'What a great swap!'

***

Mrs. Claus needed new glasses. She printed out an email from the Xmas Fairy. 'Is that an I or an O?' she asked Jack the elf.

'That's an O.'

'Good grief, Santa's shot himself!'

***

'I've got a nice clean joke for you Santa,' said Stupid the Elf.

'That'll be nice for a change.'

'What's orange and round and fat like a ball; and goes Ho ho ho?'

'I'll bite. What?'

'Fanta Claus!'

***

Santa decided to sell some of his finest reindeer breeding-stock. A little person with a speech impediment answered the ad. 'Liff me up tho I can thee into its mouff,' he demanded

Santa obliged.

'Nithe teeff,' said the little person.

'Now, liff me up tho I can thee into its eerths.'

Santa lifted him up to the right ear and then carried him around to the reindeer's left ear.

'Nithe eerths too. Now I need to thee its twat.'

Santa was fed up. He picked up the little person and stuck his head between the reindeer's back legs, then rubbed his face into the animal's private parts.

When the little person began to choke Santa put him down on the ground.

'Let me refraas that,' he spluttered.

'I just want to thee the reindeer run around!'

***

Santa called the North Pole singer Polestar, on the sleigh phone. 'Polestar, the Pope just rang to ask a favour. He wants you to write a special song and sing it at Mother Theresa's Remembrance Day tomorrow.

'I told His Holiness it would be almost impossible to write a song, and get to a remembrance ceremony on the other side of the world by tomorrow morning.'

'It's not a problem, Santa. I'll save time by getting permission to alter a song a famous friend once used, but I can do that on the flight.

'I'll feed the cat now and fly off in my trusty Lear-jet.'

'Polestar, that's amazing. What will you call Mother Theresa's song?'

'Something appropriate let me see now.

'How about "Sandals in the Bin!"

***

Xmas Eve dawned and Santa's Elves were waiting for the bottle shop to open. 'I'm not sure I should sell you any alcohol, after your last drunken binge,' the barman said.

'But, the scotch is for Santa. It fixes his constipation.'

Later, the barman dropped by the toy factory. The Elves were pissed.

'You lied to me. You assured me the scotch was for Santa's constipation.'

'And it is,' Jack the elf slurred.

'When he sees us, he'll shit himself!'

***

Santa delivered to the secret service people just as a gun battle broke out in the car park. The Chief took shelter behind Santa's sleigh. 'Our people are falling like flies,' he cried. 'Our man carrying the locations of our ware-houses has been hit. I can see his briefcase standing out there alone.'

Instantly Santa streaked across the car park, dodging bullets as he ran like the wind. He scooped up the briefcase and while still under fire, delivered it safely back to the Chief.

'Santa, you risked your life. I'm recommending you for a medal. You've saved the secret locations of all of our ware-houses.'

'Ware-houses,' Santa Yelled, 'fuckin' ware-houses?

'I thought you said Whore-houses.'

***

Santa was desperate to smuggle a snake and a skunk into the North Pole. 'I'll thread the snake thru my pants and make it look like a belt,' he told Mrs. Claus. 'And I'd like you stick the skunk down your knickers until we get thru customs.'

'That's disgusting, what about the smell?'

'Well, if it dies, it dies!'

***

Mrs. Claus complained to Santa. 'Every time you climax you let out an ear splitting yell, you must wake the whole neighbourhood.'

'Is that what you worry about, me waking the neighbours up when I climax?'

'No.

'I'm worried about you waking me up!'

***

Santa read a car magazine before going to sleep. During the night Mrs. Claus slapped him hard on the face, causing him to wake with fright. 'What's that for?' he yelled.

'For feeling my breasts and mumbling, "Big fat headlights."

'Sorry,' said Santa and went back to sleep. Soon he was slapped again.

'What now?'

'You rubbed my legs and mumbled, "Rough finish."

'Sorry,' said Santa and went back to sleep but, he was rudely awakened again by Mrs. Claus throwing him out of bed. 'Now I'm really pissed off. How dare you toss me out of my own fuckin' bed?'

'And how dare you feel my pussy and mumble, "The garage door's been left open."

***

The Xmas Fairy, her cousin Fairy Floss and blonde husband Ken were just some of the celebrities attending Santa's Xmas party.

Ken Floss woke next morning with a maxi hangover and a dim recollection of last night. 'What happened?' he asked Fairy Floss. 'Did I insult Santa?'

'You were disgustingly insulting everyone thinks you're an arsehole.'

'Well, Santa's an arrogant prick. Piss on him.'

'You did, all over his new black boots and his red cargo pants. He fired you.'

'Well, fuck him.'

'I did.

'You're back at work tomorrow!'

***

Our sex life seems a little dull lately,' Ken remarked to his lovely wife, Fairy Floss. 'How come you never tell me when you have an orgasm?' Fairy Floss looked bewildered.

'How can I tell you if you're not here!'

***

Santa and Jack the elf were drinking until the early hours of the morning. 'Santa, I wish my wife wouldn't wake up and yell abuse when I arrive home late. I switch the headlights off, coast down the driveway, take my shoes off and sneak in; and she still hears me.

'Does Mrs. Claus yell at you when you get in late from the pub?'

'No way, I honk the horn, scream into the driveway and flash the lights. I slam the door and stamp up the stairs and throw my boots into the closet. Then I jump into bed, rub my hands hard on her butt and say, 'How about a blowjob?'

'And?'

'And she's so fast asleep she can't hear me!'

***

An angry Mrs Claus met Santa at the door. 'You drunken, lying, cheating, philandering son-of-a-bitch, I hope you have a very good reason for staggering in at six in the morning.'

'Sure have,' Santa slurred.

'Breakfast!'

***

Fairy Floss was in bed. Ken walked in and handed her a glass of water and two aspirins.

'What's this for?'

'Your headache.'

'But, I don't have a headache.'

'Good.

'Let's fuck!'

***

'You and I should play magic,' Santa whispered to the Xmas Fairy.

'How do we play magic?'

'We go to your place and fuck our brains out.'

'And then?'

'And then I disappear!'

***

'How dare my wife lie to me,' Santa said to Ken Floss. 'I can't stand liars and she's a deceitful lying bitch.'

'Are you sure?'

''course I'm sure, she went out last night and didn't come home until morning. When I asked where she spent the night she said, "With the Xmas Fairy." What a shit house liar.'

'Do you have proof she's lying?'

'Course I have.

'I spent the night with the Xmas Fairy!'

***

Santa was happily banging the pretty young tourist. Just as he was about to blow his stack she yelled, 'I hope you haven't got aids. Shit, have you got aids?'

'Certainly not.'

'Well, thank shit for that.

'I sure as hell don't want aids again!'

***

Emerald, the Irish elf let Santa in on the latest gossip. 'Santa, some of those small nuns had sex with us elves on the beach last night.'

'How dare you say that, Nuns don't sleep around.'

'Really, well I'll be.

'We must have fucked some penguins!'

***

After a heavy session with the Xmas Fairy, Santa arrived home exhausted. As he staggered in the door, Mrs. Claus appeared in her red negligee, trimmed with royal-blue feather bower.

She flung her finery off to reveal a naked body and yelled, 'Sup-er Pussy!'

Santa stifled a yawn.

'Let me see now.

'Think I'll have the soup!'

***

Santa was in bed with Fairy Floss, when her phone rang. 'Who the hell was that?' Santa asked.

'Just my husband.'

'Shit, I'd better get going.'

'Relax he's just gone into an all-night poker-game with you!'

***

When Santa and the Xmas Fairy first met, they went back to her place. Santa noticed three long shelves filled with fluffy toys. Large toys on the top shelf, medium sized on the middle shelf and small ones on the bottom.

They fell into a pit of passion until it was time for Santa to go. As he was leaving he smugly asked, 'Well, how was I?'

The Xmas Fairy thought for a moment and pointed to the fluffy toys.

'You can choose anything from the bottom shelf!'

***

Why do Santa's elves only marry virgins?
Because Santa's elves can't handle criticism!

***

Mrs. Claus arrived home to find Santa in bed with a lovely young stranger. 'I'd love to hear you worm your way out of this one,' she screamed.

'Well, it's your fault,' Santa screamed back. 'she hitched a ride in the sleigh and when she told me she was hungry, I brought her home and fed her food you haven't bothered to eat. Her clothing was ragged, so I gave her shoes and a jacket you don't use anymore.

'And I was going great guns, until she was walking out the door.'

'Why, what happened?'

'She stopped and asked if there was anything else you don't use anymore?'

***

It was Santa's birthday. He hurried downstairs, anxious to receive a gift from his devoted wife but, Mrs. Claus appeared to have forgotten his birthday. 'What a bitch, I'll hurry off to work. The elves are sure to remember.'

But, the elves never mentioned his birthday.

'What a pack of pricks,' Santa fumed. He was relieved to get a message from the Xmas Fairy, inviting him to her place for lunch.

When the Xmas Fairy ushered Santa in, she was wearing a heavy jacket. 'I bet she's just back from buying my gift,' he thought. She poured him a large glass of champagne.

'Just wait here Santa, while I get this jacket off and slip into something more comfortable.'

'I know what that means,' Santa thought. He stripped naked, pulled a condom on and threw the champagne down his throat.

The Xmas Fairy appeared carrying a huge Xmas cake. Close on her heels, came Mrs. Claus, the elves, Fairy Floss and Ken singing, 'Happy birthday to you!'

***

Mrs. Claus decided to relive their first wedding anniversary and eat dinner naked. As they sat eating a delicious soup, Mrs. Claus said, 'Santa, my nipples are as hot for you today, as they were twenty years ago.'

'Why wouldn't they be,' said Santa.

'They're hanging in the friggin' soup!'

***

Santa finished deliveries to Spain and decided to have a Spanish breakfast. 'Just bring me your best dish,' he informed the friendly waiter. The waiter brought a corn omelette topped with what looked like two meat rissoles.

'Smells great, what are they?'

'Testicles from the bull that lost in the arena last night.'

'Shit, oh well when in Rome,' said Santa and he ate the appetising dish.

After delivering to Portugal, Santa flew back to Spain hoping to enjoy another Spanish omelette.

The same waiter brought the same corn dish. Santa ate with relish.

'Good, Senor Santa?' The waiter asked.

'Delicious, the small rissoles are even tastier than yesterday's large ones, it's just a shame they're so small.'

'I agree Senor Santa, but you see.

'This time the bull, he didn't lose!'

***

Because the harem housed many beautiful women, Santa took the elves along to help carry the goodies. Soon Santa, Stupid, Emerald and Jack were enjoying an orgy. The sheik strolled in and caught them. 'You must all be punished, according to your profession,' he cried.

'What do you do for a living?' He asked Stupid

'I'm a carpenter, I make Xmas toys.'

'Then we'll saw your dick off,' he turned to Jack. 'What do you do for a living?'

'Emerald and I are cutters we cut fabrics for the soft Xmas toys.'

'Then we'll cut your dicks off,' he turned to Santa. 'And Fat One, what do you do for a living?'

'Me?

'I sell lolly pops!'

***

Santa arrived at the home of Mrs. Newlywed and was surprised to find her waiting up.

'Bring the reindeer in,' she said, 'I have prepared a Xmas supper for you.'

As Santa and the reindeer got stuck into the food, their hostess led the reindeer away, one by one and made love to them. Finally she handed Santa five dollars.

He was really pissed off.

'How come the reindeer get bonked and I only get a five dollar note?'

'Well, the supper was my idea. The rest was my husband's.

He said, "Fuck the reindeer but, be sure to give Santa five dollars!"

***

Santa was cleaning the barbeque grill and fuming over Mrs. Claus's latest verbal attack. 'You know,' he remarked in a loud voice, 'this extra wide, jumbo grill is about the same width as your great big rear end.'

Mrs. Claus never said a word. She waited until late at night, when they were lying in bed. Feeling horny, Santa began making his boring, familiar moves.

Suddenly Mrs. Claus sat bolt upright and yelled, 'There is no way this top of the range, extra wide jumbo grill is going to fire up for one below average, tiny, shrivelled up excuse for a sausage!'

***

Mrs. Claus was fed up with Santa's affairs. She was contemplating divorce. Fairy Floss advised her to first consult a marriage guidance counsellor.

'I'm also a Genie,' the charming counsellor said, 'for the first session, I like to grant clients three wishes each. This usually solves all their problems.'

Santa immediately wished for his cherished possession to be longer and thicker. Mrs. Claus never said a word.

His second wish was to be able to get it up every time. Again, Mrs Claus remained silent.

Santa's third wish was to have all his elves turned into beautiful, passionate young woman. Again, Mrs. Claus stayed silent.

When it was her turn, Mrs. Claus wished to own a luxurious mansion in every capital city in the world. Santa scoffed.

For her second wish, she asked to be the wealthiest woman in the world. Santa scoffed again.

'Well come on, hurry up. Let's hear ya last fuckin' wish, ya stupid bitch.'

Mrs. Claus gave him her brightest smile.

'I wish for my husband to be gay!'

***

Ken Floss and Santa had only just left on a fishing trip, when Ken realised he'd left the keys to the cabin on the kitchen table. He dashed back and quietly entered the house.

Fairy Floss was standing naked at the sink washing the dishes. He reached out and put his hand between her legs and stroked her pussy. She groaned and spread her legs. He caressed her breasts with his other hand and thought, 'Santa will have to wait.'

Ken dropped his pants and took her from behind with passion at its best. Fairy Floss rived and moaned with every thrust.

When he'd climaxed as never before, he pulled his pants up and moved silently towards the door.

Fairy Floss spoke.

'Just one bottle of milk today please Milkman.

'Ken's gone fishing with Santa!'

***

It was early in the year and Santa was already 'working back' most nights. Mrs. Claus decided he needed a break.

'I'm taking you wining and dining,' she said.

The doorman at the club hurried forward. 'Santa, how are you this evening?'

'Have you been here before?' Mrs. Claus asked. 'Shit no. It's my Santa suit, everybody knows who I am.'

'Santa, nice to see you,' said the waitress, 'scotch on the rocks as usual?'

Mrs. Claus could smell a rat. 'I think you've been here before.'

'And I tell you I haven't. I shouldn't have worn my Santa suit. Everyone will recognise me.'

'Santa,' cried the stripper, 'will you dance naked as usual?'

'That does it,' Mrs. Claus stormed out the door and climbed into a waiting cab.

Santa raced after her and jumped in the front seat.

'Santa, my favourite passenger,' the cabbie cried.

'Looks like you picked up a real live bitch tonight!'

***

Because the Ski Lodge was over-booked, Santa, Rudolph and Stupid the elf, were forced to share a bed.

The next morning Santa said, 'I dreamed someone gave me a hand job.'

'So did I,' said Rudolph.

They both looked at Stupid.

'Well, don't look at me.

'I only dreamed I was skiing!'

***

When Santa and Mrs. Claus were first married, she had a hearing problem and found it hard to communicate after the lights were out.

'We'll just have use hand signals,' Santa said.

'What a great idea, if you want to have sex Santa, just reached over and squeeze my right breast once. If you don't want sex, just reach over and squeeze it twice.'

'That's solved my problem,' said Santa, 'now let's solve yours.

'If you want to have sex just reach over and pull my dick once. And if you don't want to have sex, just reached over and keep pulling my dick, until I get the message!'

***

Santa parked the sleigh in Lover's Lane.

'Do you want to climb into the back?' He asked the Xmas Fairy.

'Santa, don't be silly.

'I want to stay up front with you!'

***

The Mounted Police received a report that Santa was staggering around his sleigh in Lover's Lane. The pretty policewoman galloped to his rescue.

'Santa, what's happened to your reindeer? Can I help pull your sleigh?'

'Some bastard must have pinched my reindeer,' he slurred.

'And Santa, your fly's undone.'

'Oh no,' Santa looked down at his fly.

'They must have pinched the Xmas Fairy too!'

***

Santa and Mrs. Claus were still on their honeymoon when Mrs. Claus said, 'I don't want sex tonight, I just want you to hold me.'

'You're kidding?'

'I'm not. It's time you understood my emotional needs as a woman.'

Knowing he was out of luck, Santa spent the night holding her close.

The next morning he suggested they go to her favourite store. He asked her to try on three designer outfits, complete with matching shoes. As she carried them towards the waiting sales girl, Santa ushered her towards the jewellery counter and suggested she chose a diamond bracelet with matching earrings.

Mrs. Claus was shaking with excitement. 'Okay, let's hurry to the cash register,' she cried.

'No!'

'What do you mean no?'

'Well, I don't want you to buy these goodies, I just want you to fuckin' well hold them.'

'Why?'

'It's time you understood my fuckin' financial needs as a man!'

***

When Santa and Mrs. Claus were first married, Mrs. Claus wanted to know exactly how many women Santa had slept with.

'I'd rather not say, women get upset about these things.'

'I won't. Just tell me the truth and I promise never to mention it again.'

'Well, let me see. There was one, two, three, then twenty from the drama school, six from the pub, that's twenty nine. Thirty, thirty one, the eight North Pole hookers, that's thirty nine, the entire class of eighty one, say sixty nine.

'Then you, Dear. You would have been number seventy.

'Seventy one, seventy two, the cast of the strip club, that's about.........'

***

'Women are like police cars,' Santa said to Rudolph.

'Why?'

'They make a real ruckus, when they're coming!'

***

The Xmas Fairy was about to visit her grand-mother.

'Don't walk thru the North Pole forest,' Santa warned, 'the big bad wolf lives there. If he catches you, he'll suck your tits.'

The Xmas Fairy ignored Santa and skipped along the forest path. She ran into Rudolph.

'If the Big Bad wolf catches you in the forest, he'll suck your tits,' he warned.

Suddenly the Big Bad Wolf leapt out from behind a tree. 'Off with your blouse,' he yelled. 'I'm gonna suck your tits.'

'Oh no, you're not,' the Xmas Fairy cried, as she whipped off her skirt.

'You're gonna eat me all up, just like the story book says!'

***

Santa arrived in Holland. Good grief, he was reminded of a story he'd once heard, something about a heroic Dutch boy who stuck his finger in a dyke and saved the town.

So he stuck his finger in a dyke.

And she bashed the shit out of him!

***

Santa and the Xmas Fairy were having a hot lusty session on her bed. Santa was amused to notice her toes rise up, in time with the rhythm of his body. Later, when they bonked in the shower, her toes stayed still.

'How come your toes only rise up when we do it in bed?' He asked.

'Cause I take my pantyhose off in the shower, Silly!'

***

Santa staggered into the pub and begged for a glass of water. He gulped it down and followed up with six more.

'What's wrong?' the barman asked.

'I've got an insatiable nymphomaniac in the sleigh and she's worn me out. I'm supposed to go back out there, but my dick is aching and I haven't got the strength.'

'If you'll mind the bar I'll gladly go in your place. It's dark out and we're about the same build so she'll probably think I'm you.'

'Thanks,' Said Santa and the barman raced to the sleigh and fell on top of the nymphomaniac. Just as he was about to blow his stack, a police officer knocked on the window and shone his torch on the couple.

'What's going on?' The Police Officer yelled.

'Shit Officer, she's my wife!'

'Oh sorry Sir, I won't charge you. I didn't realise that the lady is your wife.'

'And I didn't either Officer, until you shone that friggen' torch!'

***

Santa was pissed off with the barman who was bragging about his strength and offering a thousand dollars reward, for anyone who could beat him at squeezing a lemon.

'How does it work?' Santa asked.

'I squeeze a fresh lemon and then hand it to my contestant. If he can squeeze one drop more, he wins the thousand dollars.'

'Can a woman enter this contest?'

'Of course.'

Santa went away and came back with a little old lady. She wore thick horn rimmed glasses and walked with a cane. After the barman stopped laughing, the contest began.

Barman squeezed his hardest. 'There's not one drop left,' he bragged as he handed over the lemon.

Quick as a flash, the little old lady squeezed what was left of the lemon and half a cup of juice ran out.

'I don't believe it,' the barman said, as he handed over his money.

'Well, I believe it,' said Santa.

'She works for the tax office!'

***

A penis, a cat and a dog waited at Santa's toy factory. 'I know Santa will give me to someone who will adore me and spoil me rotten,' said the cat.

'Me too,' said the dog, 'I know Santa will deliver me to someone who will take me on long walks and let me sleep on the bed.' He turned to the penis.

'How about you?'

'Well, the most I can hope for is for Santa will give me to someone who'll stick a bag over my head and make me do push-ups until I throw up!'

***

Santa was weaving his sleigh in and out of late night traffic, delivering toys along the New York street.

The nasty cop noticed he wasn't wearing glasses.

'Where's your licence?' He demanded. Santa handed it over.

'Just as I thought, you are supposed to wear glasses. I'm going to issue you with a hefty fine.'

'I don't need glasses because I've got contacts,' Santa said.

'I don't give a shit who you know.

'I'm going to issue you with a hefty fine!'

***

'Drinking makes you look like the most desirable woman in the world,' Santa said to Mrs. Claus.

'But I haven't been drinking, Dear.'

'No, but I have!'

***

Santa saved his best present for the childless couple. He felt blessed as he handed over the beautiful baby.

'It's a well endowed boy,' the new father told his ecstatic wife.

'No, it's a girl,' said Santa.

'You're hanging onto my thumb!'

***

Santa finished his rounds. He flew the empty sleigh home and landed in front of the toy factory. The Elves and the Xmas Fairy were listening from the darkness of the porch.

'First, I'll have a triple scotch and then I'll screw the arse off the Xmas Fairy,' Santa said to Rudolph.

The Xmas Fairy jumped from the porch in horror and ran in doors.

'There's no need to hurry,' Rudolph yelled after her.

'Santa's going to have a drink first!'

***

Mrs. Claus bought a restaurant. She made Santa Head waiter and put the Xmas Fairy in charge of the kitchen.

A blind man demanded a variety of dirty spoons, instead of a menu.

'I find it easy to order this way,' he said, as he smelled each spoon, 'hmm, Roast Beef smells nice, T/bone steak is tempting, Pheasant under Glass is tantalising but, I think I'll go with the Chicken Supreme. So move your butt, Arsehole.'

A few nights later, the blind man returned. Santa grudgingly brought him a variety of dirty spoons. 'Spaghetti smells marvellous, Macaroni and cheese is to die for but, I can't resist the Crab Thermidor. So get your arse out to the kitchen, Prick!'

A week later the blind man came in again.

Santa was waiting.

He handed a clean spoon to the Xmas Fairy and asked her to rub it back and forwards across her pussy. He then put it with the dirty spoons.

'Hmm,' said the blind man, 'The Fish Teriyaki is unbelievable, the John Dory is almost impossible to refuse, Baked Snapper is to die for, Lobster Mornay smells magnificent. He smelled the last spoon for some time.

'Hey, Dickhead,' he yelled.

'I didn't know the Xmas Fairy worked here!'

***

Although she was middle aged, the sweet lady wrote to Santa asking for a husband for Xmas.

Mrs. Claus was in charge of the mailroom.

She wrote back.

'Your request is granted, you can have mine!'

***

Santa went to the Irish bar. The bouncer came over in his new attire and sat down.

'Holy shit, I like your jacket,' Santa said.

'It's David Jones.'

'And what a great shirt.'

'David Jones.'

'Wow, what about your fabulous tie?'

'I keep telling you, David Jones.'

Just then a naked man staggered in asking for help.

'Who are you?' Santa asked.

'I'm David Jones!'

***

Mrs. Claus was fed up with Santa's egotistical behaviour. She wanted to insult him in the worst possible way.

'I had a dream about dicks being auctioned off,' she lied, 'average ones went for $10, big fat ones went for $20 and ones like yours had to be given away.'

'I had a dream too,' Santa said, 'I dreamed they were auctioning off cunts. Pretty young tight ones went for $20. Average ones went for $10 and ones like yours…'

'I know, I know,' Mrs. Claus interrupted, 'you're going to say, they had to be given away.'

'No.

'I was going to say, they held the auction in one like yours.'

***

'You selfish, mean, forgetful, unfeeling, drunken, philandering son of a bitch,' Mrs. Claus screamed, 'you've forgotten my birthday again, haven't you?'

Santa thought quickly. 'Yes, I have and it's your fault.'

'My fault?'

'Yes. The least you could do is be like other women and age a little each year. But no, you have to look exactly the same as the young girl I married.

'So how do you expect me to remember your birthday, you gorgeous bitch?'

***

The Xmas Fairy accompanied Santa on his deliveries to the jungle. They were running late.

'Why don't you place Tarzan's present under his tree house, while I go down the Witch Doctor's chimney,' Santa suggested.

The Xmas Fairy was shocked to find Tarzan pumping away at a hole in a tree.

'Poor man,' she thought, 'he's probably never had sex with a woman. I think I'll offer myself to him as a Xmas fuck.'

She quickly undressed and lay on the ground with her legs apart.

Tarzan raced over and kicked her hard in the crotch.

'What was that for?' She cried.

'Tarzan always checks for possums first!'

***

An escaped convict broke into the house as Santa and Mrs. Claus slept. Mrs. Claus wore a long flannel gown. Santa was naked.

The convict bound their hands behind and forced them to lie on the floor.

'This guy hasn't seen a woman for years,' Santa whispered, 'If he wants to have sex with you, you must go along with it and do anything he wants. Oral sex, anal sex, blowjobs, the lot, if you don't he'll probably kill us.'

'You selfish son of a bitch,' Mrs. Claus hissed, 'I would loath to have sex with him.'

'Well tough titty because you'll just have to.'

Suddenly, the convict bent over and whispered in Mrs. Claus's ear. She smiled. The convict smiled back.

'That's the girl,' Santa said, 'you won't regret putting our safety first.'

'I'm so glad you feel that way, Santa.

He just told me, you have the sexiest bum he's ever seen!'

***

Santa and Mrs. Claus were invited to the Masked Fancy Dress ball. Mrs. Claus developed a splitting headache.

'You go without me, Dear. I'll take my headache tablets and lie down for awhile.'

Santa went to the ball, dressed as the Easter Bunny.

Mrs. Claus's new headache tablets worked. After a short nap, she awoke refreshed and decided to go to the ball.

She arrived to find the Easter Bunny swilling his drinks down and feeling up every woman on the dance floor.

Mrs. Claus was furious. She knew that because Santa hadn't seen her costume, he couldn't recognise her.

She followed him out to the patio and when he whispered disgusting suggestions in her ear, she let him have his way with her on the patio. He tried every position in the book. And more!

An exhausted Mrs. Claus went home, packed her costume away and waited.

At 3am Santa arrived with his bunny suit over one arm.

'Did you have a good time?' Mrs. Claus demanded, 'did you dance with everyone?'

'No. I walked thru the door to find Rudolph waiting. He and the elves had a poker game going in the basement and we played all night.

'I lent my costume to Sucha Sleaze. He said the Easter Bunny suit was a hit.

'He and some big fat lady fucked their brains out for hours!'

***

Santa arrived at the department store, ready for a full day of listening to children's Xmas requests. He'd stopped off on the way to buy a big bag of crabs from the fish markets. A pretty young supervisor suggested he pop them in the staff room refrigerator.

Just before closing time, the pretty young supervisor called over the PA system.

'Santa this is Stephanie, the girl you gave the crabs to. If you drop by the staff room, I'll make sure you get the crabs again, before you go home!'

***

Santa jumped the Xmas Fairy as she was fed the turkeys and listened to their calls of 'Gobble, gobble gobble.'

'I'm going to gobble you all up,' Santa whispered in her ear, 'gobble, gobble gobble.'

'I'm sick to death of gobble, gobble gobble,' the Xmas Fairy screamed.

'Doesn't anyone fuck around here anymore?'

***

Fairy Floss asked Santa to look after her soft drink sales department, while she embarked on a well-earned vacation.

'But, I won't know what to do,' he said.

'Oh, it's easy. I'll give you a list of our buyers. They're all female.

'Just call on about a dozen each day and knock 7 UP!'

***

'Do you think Fairy Floss is a bit naïve?' Rudolph asked Santa.

'Sure do. Would you believe, she thought 7 UP was a soft drink before she met my seven elves!'

***

Santa's toy factory urgently needed funds. He let the world know and hundreds of concerned senior citizens queued up to donate a dollar.

Mrs. Claus was in charge of the donations. One elderly man waited in line for 20 minutes, before loosing his cool. He waved a cheque in the air and yelled.

'I'm damned if I'm going to wait in this friggin' line any longer. Where's the dick-head who runs this joint?'

'I don't allow bad language in this office,' Mrs. Claus yelled back, 'if you swear again you will have to leave.'

'Well, up yours Lady. This cheque's losing interest while I'm piddling around waiting for you to move your fat arse.'

'I will not tolerate this type of abuse, out!'

'Out your fucking self, go get the manager so he can hear the shit I have to put up with.'

Santa arrived. 'What's all the yelling and screaming about?'

'This man is using disgusting language.'

'Hey, all I'm trying to do here is donate this fuckin' cheque for five million dollars and get back to my board meeting.'

Santa looked at the cheque and then at the man.

'And this fuckin' bitch won't help you?'

***

The old farmer asked Santa for a rooster for his chicken pen for Xmas.

'I'll bring you a super rooster,' said Santa, 'one capable of servicing all your hens.'

The rooster did more than service the hens. After he'd given the hens a thorough going over, he raced to the duck yard, then on to the sheep, pigs and finally a flock of geese. Over the next twenty-four hours, he banged anything that moved.

When Rooster stopped for a few minutes to eat, the farmer grabbed him.

'I want you to slow down. You're doing a great job but, if you keep this pace up you'll drop dead. Do you understand?'

The rooster nodded. When the farmer let him go however, he flew off and started on the hens again.

'He'll never learn. I bet he's dead by morning.'

And sure enough, the next morning, the old man found Rooster lying flat on his back in the yard with buzzards circling overhead.

'Oh, Rooster, I begged you to slow down, but you wouldn't listen. And now you're as good as gone.'

Rooster opened one eye and shushed the old farmer.

'Be quiet,' he whispered.

'The friggin' buzzards are getting closer!'

***

Santa and Mrs. Claus were stranded on a desert island. One day, the Xmas Fairy washed up on the beach. She and Santa couldn't wait to get their rocks off. Mrs. Claus had other ideas.

'Now we'll have three people doing eight hour shifts in the watch house, instead of two people doing twelve hour shifts.'

'I'm only too pleased to help,' the Xmas Fairy said to Santa, 'but, how are we going to fuck with her watching our every move? I'll have to think of an idea.'

The Xmas Fairy took first watch. Mrs. Claus made a fire while Santa cleaned the fish for supper.

'Please stop fucking down there,' the Xmas Fairy suddenly yelled from the top of the coconut tree 'do you hear me? Stop fucking.'

'We are not fucking,' an indignant Mrs. Claus yelled back.

'Yes you are. I can clearly see you fucking.'

'Well, we're not.'

'Yes, you are.'

The Xmas Fairy continued her accusations thru-out her shift. When she came down, she whispered to Santa.

'While you're on watch, accuse us of fucking.'

Santa climbed to the top and as the Xmas Fairy took a nap on the sand and Mrs. Claus milked a few coconuts, Santa yelled down.

'Will you two stop fucking?'

'We are not,' the girls yelled back, 'we are definitely not.'

'I can see you clearly and I don't care what you say, you're fucking.' Finally it was Mrs. Claus's turn to take watch. Santa and the Xmas Fairy tore their clothes off and leapt on each other.

Mrs. Claus watched for a few moments, before yelling down. 'You're both right, I cannot believe my eyes.

'From up here, it looks just like you're fucking!'

***

The midget met Fairy Floss at Santa's Xmas party. He was captivated by her voluptuous figure and told her he could give her the best orgasms ever. They went back to her place and stripped to their birthday suits.

'Lie down, close your eyes and spread your legs,' he said.

Soon Fairy Floss felt an extremely well endowed organ inside her. She achieved multiple orgasms until she begged him to stop.

'If you think that was great,' said the Little Person.

'Just wait 'til I get both legs in!'

***

Santa delivered to the handicapped. They were having a swimming contest. The contestants lined up for the first heat. One man was armless, another legless and the third had no body at all, just a head.

The whistle blew and the contestants hit the water with a splash. The armless man took the lead. The legless guy soon began to gain. The head sank straight to the bottom.

Santa dived in and rescued the head. He successfully applied mouth to mouth. The head spluttered and coughed.

'Oh shit you're just a head,' Santa cried, 'you must have known you'd sink.'

'I did not know I'd sink,' the head yelled back, 'I've spent seven days a week for three years, learning to swim with my fucking ears.

'And just before the whistle blows, some arsehole prick sticks a swimming cap on my head!'

***

The beautiful buxom blonde awoke as Santa placed a gift in her stocking.

'Santa, I'm so embarrassed to be caught sleeping in my birthday suit. Where on earth is my night gown?'

'It's over on the chair, next to my Santa suit.'

***

A beautiful buxom blonde in a slinky red negligee waited for Santa to come down the chimney.

'Santa, all I want for Xmas is for you to fulfil my fantasy about having sex with Santa.'

'You and everyone else, sorry not enough friggen' time.'

Beautiful buxom blonde allowed her negligee to fall to the floor.

'Wow, great tits and great bush,' said Santa. She poked her long red tongue thru luscious, red lips and made suggestive licking movements.

'Great tongue.'

She turned her back, bent over from the waist and wriggled her derriere.

'Great arse. Oh shit, I'll have to stay.

'I can't fit up the fuckin' chimney!'

***

Santa returned with the empty sleigh. 'I bet you're glad that's over for another year,' said Stupid the Elf.

'Sure am. The first thing I'm going to do is rip the wife's pants off.'

'Why?'

'Cause the elastic's so tight, they're killing me!'

***

Santa noticed the beautiful blonde sitting alone at the bar. He and his koala friend moved over and sat next to her.

'He's really cute,' the girl said, 'does he do any tricks?'

'Yes. He sucks pussy.'

After a few drinks, Santa convinced her to try the koala, so they went to her apartment.

'Take all your clothes off, lie down and spread your legs.'

Santa sat the koala between her legs and waited.

Nothing happened.

Suddenly, Santa put his hands on his hips and glared at the koala. 'Okay, take notice.

'This is the very last time I show you how to suck pussy!'

***

Santa and Mrs. Claus were lying in bed.

'Darling, I have to make love to you,' Santa said.

'Can't,' she said, 'I have an appointment with my gynaecologist in the morning and he would know if I had sex tonight. I'd be embarrassed.'

The more Santa tried to sleep, the hornier he got. He rolled over and nudged Mrs. Claus.

'Can I ask if you have a dental appointment tomorrow?'

***

The elderly shoe salesman was assisting Mrs. Claus. From where he sat, he could see she wasn't wearing knickers.

'If I was a few years younger,' he suddenly said, 'I'd fill your pussy with ice cream and eat it all out.'

Mrs. Claus was shocked. She went straight to the toy factory.

'Santa, you'll have to kick the shoe salesman's butt. He said he'd like to fill my pussy with ice cream and eat it all out.'

'You'll have to kick his butt, yourself.'

'Why?'

'Cause I'm not messing with anyone, who can eat that much ice cream!'

***

Mrs. Claus was about to leave for the airport. The phone rang and she picked it up. The caller spoke first.

Mrs. Claus listened for a moment and then said.

'How the hell would I know? I'm not the weather girl.'

'Who was that?' Santa asked.

'The Xmas Fairy, wanting to know if the coast is clear!'

***

Santa was fed up with the elves taking time off work. 'You'll have to be dead or in the hospital, to be excused tomorrow,' he yelled.

'What if I'm suffering from severe sexual exhaustion?' Stupid asked and everyone fell apart with laughter.

When the ruckus died down, Santa scowled at Stupid.

'Not fuckin' good enough.

'You'll just have to saw with your left hand, instead of the right!'

***

'Cheer up,' Santa said to Ken Floss, 'It's been weeks since you found your wife in bed with someone else. You have to get on with life.'

'It's easy for you to talk. What would you do, if you found Mrs. Claus in bed with another man?'

'Hmmm, I'd probably break his white cane in half and kick his Seeing Eye Dog up the bum!'

***

'Shit, Rudolph!' Santa said, 'I'm going to be a father at last.'

'Congratulations, Santa! How's Mrs. Claus taking the news?'

'Keep your voice down and hope like hell, she never finds out!'

***

Santa took his dog Wonder into the new bar. 'Sorry, no dogs allowed,' said the barmaid.

'Bugger this,' said Wonder, 'let's go somewhere else.'

The barmaid couldn't believe her ears.

'Please stay and let the dog talk to me.'

When Santa went to the little boy's room, the barmaid asked Wonder if he would go out the back and frighten her boss, by saying 'Hello.'

She gave him $20 and away he went.

Wonder didn't return.

When Santa came back, he was furious. 'Someone might pinch him. I've never let him out alone since he learned to talk.'

They found Wonder out back, screwing the arse off a gorgeous French Poodle.

'Wonder, I've never known you to do this before,' Santa cried.

'Of course not.

'I've never had $20 before!'

***

Santa and Mrs. Claus were dining at a very expensive restaurant. 'Can I order anything I want?' Mrs. Claus asked.

'Of course you can't, you stupid bitch. Order what Wonder would like.

'Didn't you hear me tell him, we'll bring him a doggie bag?'

***

What are the three best things about having Alzheimer's?

You can hide your own Xmas presents under the tree.

You can save money by reading the same newspaper everyday.

You can hide your own Xmas presents under the tree.

***

Santa taught Mrs. Claus's two female parrots to squawk, 'Who wants to fuck? Who wants to fuck?' Mrs. Claus was embarrassed and asked the parish priest for help.

'I have two devout male parrots. They pray all day,' he said, 'bring your parrots over and let them stay awhile.'

When Mrs. Claus and her parrots arrived, she was very impressed to hear the male parrots praying as they chewed on their rosary beads. The priest opened the cage door and popped her parrots in.

'Who wants to fuck, who wants to fuck?' Her parrots squawked.

'Thank you Jesus,' the male parrots screeched.

'Our prayers are answered!'

***

Santa returned from his very first delivering to the Moon. 'How did you go? What was it like?' The elves asked.

'I was disappointed. It was a bit fuckin' dull.

'No fuckin' atmosphere at all!'

***

Santa finished his rounds and was getting his rocks off in the back of the sleigh with the Xmas Fairy.

Young Trash Sleaze hopped up and took a photo of the lustful two. Santa ran after him and asked for the film. Trash offered to sell the camera and film for $5,000.

'You shock me. I'm the one who gave you the camera for Xmas.'

'I could sell the camera to Mrs. Claus,' Trash jeered. Santa bought the camera.

'Nice camera,' said Mrs. Claus.

'I should hope so. It cost $5,000.'

'Good grief,' cried Mrs. Claus.

'Some bastard must have seen you coming!'

***

'Rudolph asked the priest if the church regarded sex as work or play. 'Play of course, that's why it's not permitted on Sunday.'

'Bugger this,' said Rudolph, not happy with the answer, 'the priest wouldn't have a clue. I think I'll ask Santa.

'Sex is definitely not work,' Santa said.

'If it were work, Mrs. Claus would have the maid do it!'

***

Santa delivered some big pots of the best honey to the little orphan bear in the cave. He put the honey under the almost dead Xmas tree and noticed the little orphan bear looked almost dead, too.

'Santa told you to be sure to hibernate all winter Teddy. Didn't you hear me?'

'Bugger,

'I thought you said, 'Masturbate all winter!''

***

Santa stepped out of the sleigh. He still had the whip in his hand. The Xmas Fairy was watching a game of tennis. Santa strolled over and slapped his hand with the whip, as he concentrated on the tennis.

'Whose game?' He asked.

The Xmas fairy looked at the whip.

'Me!' She cried.

'I'm game!'

***

'Santa, the Xmas Fairy is so vain. I wonder why she spends so much time improving her appearance and hardly any time improving her mind.'

'Well, the Xmas Fairy understands men.

'She knows that men aren't blind!'

***

Rain, hail or shine, Santa and Mrs. Claus always played their weekly game of golf together.

'Santa if I die before you, will you marry again?' She asked.

'Ooh, yes!' Santa answered, a little too fast.

Mrs. Claus was hurt and offended.

'Would you let the second Mrs. Claus use my golf clubs?'

'Of course not.

'The Xmas Fairy doesn't like golf!'

***

'Some men are bastards!' Mrs. Claus said to Santa, 'Ken Floss traded his lovely wife Fairy Floss, for a season's football ticket. You wouldn't do that would you Dear?'

'Of course not, Ken must be mad.

'The football season's almost over!'

***

Santa's sleigh crashed in a deep ravine. He rang for help on the sleigh phone. The rescue chopper appeared overhead and a loud speaker announced, 'Red Cross here, we're sending someone down.'

'Red Cross,' Santa yelled back, 'piss off.'

'I fuckin' well donated at the office!'

***

'Santa, I've been cheating on my wife and cheating on the tax man,' Rudolph said, 'can you tell me what will happen if I get caught?'

'Well,' said Santa, after thinking it over, 'If you get caught, the taxman is still gonna want to screw you!'

***

The Xmas fairy battered her eyes at Santa. 'I hope I don't get randy eating all this Xmas cake,' she said.

'There is a cake that actually reduces a woman' sex drive by 99%.'

'Really Santa, what is it?'

'Wedding Cake!'

***

It was almost midnight. Santa and the Xmas Fairy parked the sleigh next to the teenage couple's car in Lover's Lane. They noticed the young girl sitting alone in the back seat, filing her nails by the light of the moon.

A young man sat in the front, quietly reading a novel by torchlight.

Santa was intrigued. He wandered over. 'How old are you?' He asked the young man.

'Eighteen.'

'How old is your girlfriend?'

The boy looked at his watch.

'In exactly five minutes, she too, will be eighteen!'

***

'The Xmas Fairy smells nice,' Rudolph remarked to Santa, 'must be what she puts behind her ears to please you.'

'Really,' Santa looked puzzled.

'You mean her knees!'

***

When Santa and Rudolph finished delivering to Paris they stopped off to enjoy a beer in the sinful city.

'I wonder how French woman hold their liquor,' Rudolph said.

'Well, from my experience, it's usually by the ears!'

***

Santa was invited to the brand new shopping centre to meet the children and hear their requests.

He arrived, wearing an old Davy Crocket hat with a long fox tail.

'Santa, why are you wearing that furry hat?' A sweet little girl asked.

'It's Mrs Claus's idea.

'I told her I wasn't sure what to wear to New Town and she said, 'Where the fock's that?'

***

When Santa finally arrived home, he was very late and very pissed. Mrs. Claus had taken a course in reverse psychology.

Instead of nagging and yelling at Santa, she welcomed him in, undressed him, gave him a relaxing bath and led him to a table where delicious refreshments awaited. While he ate by the soft romantic candlelight, she climbed under the table and gave him head for the first time.

When he was thoroughly satisfied, she whispered, 'Come on, I think it's time we went to bed.'

'We'll have to be quick well,' Santa slurred, 'if I'm late home, the old bat will jump and scream, and piss and fart, and choke and swear, and scratch my eyes out, and throw knives, and break dishes and cast spells, and kick me in the groin, and cry and foam at the mouth and hiss and…………..'

***

Santa and Mrs. Claus were having an argument.

'And you're a lousy lover,' she shouted.

Later, she thought she should apologise.

She called Santa on his sleigh phone. 'What are you doing Dear, are you busy?'

'Of course I'm friggin' busy.

'I'm in the middle of getting a second opinion!'

***

Mrs. Claus needed an emergency appendectomy. She drifted up, out of her body and saw God. 'Is my time is up?' she asked.

'Good God no, you have thirty three glorious years left.'

'Thank you God. I'll live life to the full.'

Mrs. Claus stayed on at the hospital and in one day, received a facelift, a body nip and tuck, a boob lift and liposuction. On her way home from hospital she went straight to the beauty salon for professional make up and a change of hair colour.

Later, as she hurried across the street to buy a trendy new outfit, a truck ran her down and left her as 'dead as a doornail.'

When she arrived at the Pearly Gates she yelled at God. 'You assured me I had thirty three years left!'
'Sorry Mrs. Claus.

'I just didn't recognise you!'

***

Stupid the elf saw the truck slam into Mrs. Claus. He ran to tell Santa.

'Stupid woman,' Santa cried. 'If only she'd gone straight back to the kitchen after he appendectomy!'

***

Stupid the elf finally married. 'My wife is an angel,' he said to Santa.

'Shit you're lucky.

'Mine's still living!'

***

Mrs. Claus asked Santa again, for more money for the Xmas shopping.

'Good grief, Woman,' he shouted, 'every week you expect more money. Sometimes I think you need friggin' brains more than you need money.'

'You're probably right, Dear. That's why I asked for what I thought you have the frigging most of!'

***

Santa needed a cigarette after a heavy bonking session with the Xmas Fairy. He asked for a light. 'Top drawer of my dresser,' she said.

Santa noticed a photo of a handsome young man next to the lighter. 'Is this your husband?'

'Don't be silly,' she laughed.

'Your boyfriend?'

The Xmas Fairy doubled up with laughter. 'Santa you are really stupid.

'That's me before my sex change!'

***

Monday morning arrived. Santa summoned Jack the elf to his office. 'Did your Grandfather's funeral go okay on Friday?'

Jack played for time. 'It was a horrible wet windy day, Santa.'

'I wouldn't worry too much. The weather forecast is fine for Thursday. Your grief stricken mother just phoned.

'Seems there's a full replay of Grandfather's funeral this Thursday!'

***

Santa came home in really bad mood. 'Problems at work, Dear?' Mrs. Claus asked.

'Yes. Jack the elf took the afternoon off to attend his Grandmother's funeral. I thought it was the old trick to go see the cricket, so of course I was forced to waste the entire afternoon following him around.'

'And how was the cricket, Dear?' Mrs. Claus smiled.

'Cricket?

'It was a fuckin' boring afternoon at his Grandmother's funeral!'

***

Santa's snow mobile broke down. Fairy Floss and husband Ken were walking home from the pub. They stopped to help.

'What seems to be the trouble?' Ken asked.

'Fuckin' piston broke,' said Santa.

'Yeah, so are we.

'We know how you feel!'

***

Santa and the elves were having a few drinks after work. Santa put a photo of Mrs. Claus on the bar in front of him.

'You must love your wife very much,' the barman remarked.

'Not really,' said Santa, 'I use it as a timer. When she starts to look good, I know I'm half pissed.

'So I go home!'

***

The day Santa dreaded finally arrived. Today Mrs. Claus would take her first driving lesson.

'Where do I start, what on earth should I do Dear?' She asked.

'You know all those things you're always telling me to do, when you're back-seat driving?

'Yes Dear.'

'Well, just sit in the fuckin' front seat and do them yourself!'

***

Santa left a jumbo pack of condoms under the tree of Mr and Mrs Senior Citizen. 'I thought seniors didn't need to worry about pregnancy!' Rudolph remarked to Santa.

'No, it's not that.

'They both love the smell of burning rubber!'

***

The front door slammed shut, locking Mrs. Claus out. While she yelled to get back in, Santa's dog Wonder barked at the back door.

Stupid the elf hurried to the front to let Mrs. Claus in.

'No,' Santa yelled, 'let Wonder in first.'

'Why?'

'Because the dog will shut the fuck up when he gets in, that's why!'

***

Mrs. Claus and Santa were having another 'domestic.' 'I should have listened to Mother,' she wailed, 'she tried to stop me from marrying you.'

Santa was shocked. 'I never knew. I had no idea. I must go to dear Mother-In-Law immediately.

'Oh, how I've wronged that woman!'

***

Rudolph and Santa were having a quiet drink. 'What's bothering you Santa?' Rudolph asked.

'It's the Xmas Fairy. She's only giving me oral sex once a week now.'

'I wouldn't be too worried if I were you.

'She's cut the rest of us right out!'

***

Rudolph and Dancer's honeymoon was coming to an end. 'Darling I have a confession to make,' she said, 'I didn't like to tell you before our wedding but, I suffer from asthma.'

'Thank goodness,' Rudolph sobbed.

'All this time, I thought you were hissing at me!'

***

Santa and Mrs Claus revisited their honeymoon hotel to celebrate their 25th anniversary.

'Santa, what where your thoughts when you first saw me naked?'

'I just wanted to fuck your brains out and suck your tits dry.'

'And now.'

'I think I've done a pretty good job!'

***

Santa and Ken Floss were having a drink when Ken's wife Fairy Floss, walked up to the new bartender. She looked into his eyes and in a husky voice, asked to see the manager.

'I am the manager,' he said as he took her hand. He looked deep into her eyes and slowly kissed her fingers, 'what can I do for the most beautiful girl in the bar? Your wish is my command.'

"Well, you can start by organising some toilet paper for the Little Girl's Room.

'I had to wipe my arse with my fingers!'

***

Ken Floss, Fairy Floss's blond husband came home unexpectedly and found her naked and panting on the bed. She thought quickly. 'Call the doctor Dear I think I'm having a heart attack.'

As her husband ran to call the doctor, their small son Fairyboy began to cry. 'Santa's in the closet and he's got no clothes on.'

Ken Floss yanked the closet door open.

'Jesus Santa, my wife's having a heart attack and you're fooling around scaring the shit out of our kid!'

***

Mrs. Claus dreamed of romance as their wedding anniversary drew close. She booked herself and Santa into an isolated cabin, far away from his low-life friends. The cabin was freezing and Santa had to go chop wood for the fire.

He came in after a few minutes, complaining about his cold hands. Mrs. Claus got him to put his hands between her thighs until they warmed up. When they were warm, he went back and chopped more wood.

He soon returned and again placed his cold hands between her thighs.

'What's the problem with your dam ears?' Mrs. Claus yelled.

'Don't they ever get cold?'

***

'Santa, ever since my wife caught me playing around she's been cold towards me,' said Rudolph, 'I put a hot water bottle in her bed the other night and it turned to ice.'

'You think that's cold? Hell, even when my wife wants to have sex, the furnace kicks in!'

***

'Do you want to see what I got the Xmas Fairy for Xmas?' Santa asked Fairy Floss.

'Yes, please.'

Santa un-wrapped a full-length fur coat, made from the skins of protected Tigers. Fairy Floss was horrified.

'Do you know how many animals from the endangered species list were killed just to make that bloody coat?' She yelled.

'Yes, of course I do, but I didn't know I had a witness.

'Bugger, now I'll have to kill you too!'

***

Two North Pole fleas agreed to meet at the beach for a holiday in the sun. The first flea arrived in comfort. He travelled in the warm fuzz of a pretty flight attendant's pussy. The second one arrived with chattering teeth and a shivering body. He'd travelled on the moustache of a Bikie, riding on a Harley.

'You made the same mistake last year,' the first flea argued, 'didn't I tell you to go to the airport, hop on a female flight attendant, crawl into her knickers and relax in her warm fuzz?'

'And I did, I did. But, I dozed off just as we were coming in to land and later I woke up in her warm pussy, in the back seat of her car at the airport.

'And the next thing I know, I was right back on the bikie's moustache!'

***

The poor man asked Santa for a Genie in a bottle for Xmas. Santa delivered the goods. Santa was shocked when the police called and asked him to come straight to the poor man's home.

The little shack had been replaced with a mansion filled with gorgeous young woman wearing scanty attire. 'That was probably his first wish,' Santa said to the police, 'I can understand that.'

As the police led him thru the mansion towards the landscaped rear gardens, Santa noticed the floors were carpeted with $1,000 bills. 'Probably his second wish and I can understand that too.'

As they walked towards a massive oak tree, Santa was shocked to see the poor man's body hanging by a bridle from a branch.

'That would have been his third and last wish,' Santa said sadly.

'And I can't for the life of me understand why anyone would want to be hung like a donkey!'

***

Santa was about to take the Xmas Fairy home when she said, 'how about I stay naked and lick your dick all the way home?'

'You're on,' Santa agreed but, he got so fired up he crashed the sleigh and got stuck behind the wheel.

'Go and get help,' he yelled.

'I can't go naked.'

'Sure you can. Just hold my boot over your snatch.'

The Xmas Fairy finally found an all night service station.

'Please can you help us?' She begged the attendant, 'Santa crashed and now he's stuck.'

'Shit. You'll need the Search and Rescue department.

'I think he's in too far!'

***

Santa finished deliveries to Italy. As he was about to fly home, an Italian man dashed out of the alley and held a knife to Santa's throat.

'Unzippa your pants anda masturbate righta now,' he demanded.

Santa had no choice but to comply.

'Nowa do it again two more times or I a killa you right now.'

By the time Santa finally finished for the third time, he was puffing and panting, gasping for breath and holding his heart.

'Very good.

'Now you canna flya my sister home!'

***

Santa walked into the bar and was stunned to see a twelve-inch piano player. 'Well, fuck my brains out. Where on earth did you get a twelve-inch piano player?'

'Well, I found this bottle and whenever I rub it a Genie comes out and grants a wish.'

'Shit, I'd like to try that.' Santa grabbed the bottle and rubbed it and out came the Genie.

'I'd like a million bucks, please Genie.'

A million ducks flew in the door and crapped all over Santa. 'Oh fuck, I asked for a million bucks, not a million ducks.'

'I know how you feel,' said the barman.

'There's no way I asked for a twelve inch pianist!'

***

Times were tough and Santa was cutting costs. He yelled at Mrs. Claus. 'You lazy bitch, if you took the trouble to learn to iron we wouldn't need an ironing lady. And if you took the trouble to learn to clean the house, we wouldn't need a cleaning man.

'And if you would only learn to fuck,' Mrs. Claus yelled back.

'We wouldn't need a gardener!'

***

Mrs. Claus hurried to Santa's factory. 'Come home and pack your bags Santa. I've just won the $50 million dollar lottery.'

'Holy shit, shall I pack for the sun or the shops?

'Who cares?

'I just want you out of the house by midday!'

***

Mrs. Claus was lunching with her mother. She invited the Xmas Fairy to join them. After a few glasses of champagne, the talk turned to Santa.

'Mother and I were cleaning out Santa's study on Monday,' Mrs. Claus confided, 'and I found a pile of pornographic magazines.'

The Xmas Fairy feigned shock. 'How awful, whatever did you do?'

'Threw them out of course!'

'And I found a packet of condoms,' Mother-in-law piped up.

'That's dreadful, what did you do?'

'Poked holes in all of them!'

And Fairy Floss fainted!

***

Santa and the Xmas Fairy were almost run down by a Porsche. 'There's not much difference between a Porsche and a porcupine,' Santa fumed as they struggled to their feet.

'Really Santa, what's the difference?'

'Well, with a porcupine the prick's on the outside!'

Dead

When Santa finally went to a doctor, he was told he wouldn't make it thru the night.

Mrs. Claus was devastated. 'Santa, I will make sure this is the best night of your life.'

She cooked a sumptuous meal and set the table with the finest china and crystal. She ordered six bottles of the world's most expensive champagne from the bottle shop. Next she gave Santa a naughty massage and made passionate love to him for hours. He was overwhelmed.

When she fell asleep with exhaustion, he tapped her on the shoulder and suggested they start all over again.

An hour later, Mrs. Claus fell asleep. Santa woke her and shoved his most cherished possession in her mouth.

Next Santa tried every position in the Karma Sutra. Twice! Mrs. Claus was exhausted. Santa had to shake her awake again. 'Let's fuck 'til daylight,' he said.

'No way.'

'Why not?'

'Well, unlike some people I have to get up in the morning!'

***

When Santa died, Mrs. Claus insisted on cremation. She brought his ashes home and emptied them on the outdoor table.

'Santa, remember the world trip you always promised me? Well, I bought a first class ticket with the insurance money. And remember the new car you always promised me? Well, I bought a new Mercedes from the insurance money. And remember the diamond ring you always promised me? I bought the one I always wanted from the insurance money.

'And Santa, remember that blowjob I promised you?

'Well, look out here it comes!'

***

'You have only a few hours left,' Doctor said to Santa as he lay on his deathbed in a room next to the kitchen. Santa smelled his favourite cookies baking. He summoned all his strength, got off the bed, crawled to the kitchen and managed to pull himself up on chair.

He reached for a cookie. Mrs. Claus slapped his hand away.

'Don't touch,' she screamed.

'They're for your Funeral Guests!'

***

Santa was on his deathbed. He beckoned Mrs. Claus to come close. She saw the tears in his eyes.

'There's something I'd like to say before I go,' he said.

'Yes, Dear I'm listening.'

'Well, just after we were married, I crashed the sleigh and couldn't walk for six months.'

'I know Dear and I nursed you back to health.'

'Then the toy factory burned down and it wasn't insured.'

'Yes Dear and I was by your side all thru that trauma.'

'And then, as soon as I managed to rebuild, things went bad and I was forced into bankruptcy.'

'And I was by your side the whole time. Santa, what is it you wish to tell me?'

'That you're nothing but a bad-luck fuckin' jinks!'

***

Santa and the Xmas Fairy made a pact. The first one to die would come back and inform the other of the After Life. Santa went first and true to his promise, he contacted the Xmas Fairy one dark, lonely night.

'I'mmm… baaaaackkk. I'mmm…..baaaaackkk.'

'Oh my goodness is that you Santa?'

'Yeeesss! I have managed to get thru to tell you of the After Life. I have sex before breakfast each morning and after a delicious breakfast I have long leisurely sex until lunch. Then I lie in the sun or do whatever I want until I feel horny again.

'I have sex whenever I want and I have the stamina to go all day and all night with multiple partners.'

'Santa, you must surely be an angel in Heaven.'

'No, I'm not an angel in Heaven.

'I'm a friggin' rabbit in Texas!'

***

Santa died from diarrhoea. Mrs. Claus issued a press release announcing to the world, that Santa died from gonorrhoea.

'Why on earth did you announce he died from gonorrhoea and not diarrhoea?' The shocked Xmas Fairy asked.

'It was his publicist's idea. She thought it best Santa be remembered as a great lover, instead of the great shit he really was!'

***

Santa delivered to the mermaids. About twenty metes down, he bumped into a man without scuba gear. Santa grabbed his waterproof chalk board and scribbled, 'How the fuck can you stay down without scuba gear?'

He pushed his chalk and board into the guy's hands. The guy scribbled back.

'Cause I'm drowning!'

***

Santa died and went straight to hell. 'We're not too harsh, down here,' the devil said, we do give you a choice as to how you spend eternity.'

He opened the first door to reveal a politician hanging from the ceiling with a fire burning underneath.

'I'll skip that one,' Santa said.

'No problem you have another choice.' He opened the second door and Santa was stunned to see an American president chained to the wall. A well known White House employee was on her knees, giving him a blowjob.

Quick as a flash, Santa said, 'I choose this one.'

'Done,' said the devil.

'Hey White House Employee, you've been replaced!'

Chauvinist

'Santa, I wish I had a blonde girlfriend like the Xmas Fairy,' said Rudolph.

'You'd be better off getting a brick.'

'Why?'

'Cause a brick won't follow you home after you lay it!'

***

'Not all blondes are dumb, Santa. I know one who's very smart.'

'Yeah, I bet she's a golden retriever!'

***

'What are you gonna do Santa, if the Xmas Fairy starts smoking?'

'Probably slow down and use some lubricant.'

***

'Look,' Santa called to Fairy Floss, 'there's a dead bird.'

Fairy Floss looked up to the sky.

'Where, where?'

***

'Santa, why is Fairy Floss throwing bread into the toilet?' Rudolph asked.

'To feed the toilet ducts!'

***

'Santa, what is it when a woman talks dirty to a man?'

'Oh, it's about $5 per minute.'

'And what is it when a man talks dirty to a woman?'

'It's sexual harassment!'

***

'Does the Xmas Fairy like the lights on or off when you're having sex, Santa?'

'Off.

'When she wants them on she opens the car door!'

***

Santa and Rudolph were having a quite beer when the local lawyer walked past. 'What's she like Santa?' Rudolph asked.

'I'd rather have a hooker any day.'

'Why?'

'Cause a hooker stops screwing you after you're dead!'

***

'Where's Fairy Floss?' The Xmas Fairy asked Santa.

'She's inside staring at a can of tomato juice.'

'Why?'

'Cause it says concentrate!'

***

'Santa, I have to make a choice between my wife and my job.'

'That's easy, choose the job.

'Why?'

'Well, after a year your job will still suck!'

***

'Fairy Floss threw a grenade at me,' Santa announced to a shocked Rudolph.

'What did you do?'

'I pulled the fuckin' pin out and threw it back!

***

'Santa, why was alcohol invented?'

'So ugly girls could get laid at Xmas!'

***

Santa called in to see Ken Floss. Fairy Floss said he was due home any minute. She wore a see thru blouse and no bra.

You have great tits,' Santa remarked, 'I'll give you a hundred bucks for a look at one.'

Fairy Floss thought for a moment. 'What the hell. It's only a look and a hundred bucks is a hundred bucks.' She unbuttoned her blouse and revealed one gorgeous breast.

Without taking his eyes away, Santa took a hundred dollar note from his pocket and threw it on the table.

'Show me both,' he drooled, 'and I'll give you another hundred.'

Fairy Floss revealed a perfect pair and Santa looked long and hard. Finally he threw down his second hundred dollar note and left.

'You just missed Santa,' Fairy Floss said to Ken.

'Bugger but, not to worry.

'I see he's dropped off the two hundred bucks he owes me!'

***

'Santa, I was having a beer with the Xmas Fairy and she asked if I knew how many men it takes to open a bottle of beer?'

'Well, she can get nicked, Rudolph.

It should be open when she brings it to a man!'

***

Rudolph called Santa. 'Santa I think my wife might be dead. How can I tell?'

'Quick check your sex life and your laundry.'

'And?'

'If your sex life's the same but your laundry's piled up, she's probably dead!'

***

'Santa, Mrs. Claus crosses the road a lot. Where does she go?' Stupid asked.

'Never mind about that, what the fuck is she doing out of the kitchen?'

***

'Santa my dishwasher's stopped working!'

'Shit, Stupid. Go and yell at her!'

***

'There goes the North Pole virgin,' Stupid said to Santa.

'Yeah, you've heard of a walking time-bomb well, virgins are like a walking time-balloon.'

'What's a walking time-balloon?'

'One prick and it's all over!'

***

'I'm thinking of having surgery to enlarge my boobs,' Mrs. Claus announced to Santa.

'You don't need surgery. Just rub toilet paper between your boobs every day.'

'And that works?'

'Well, it sure as hell worked for your big fat arse!'

***

When Santa and Mrs. Claus went on their honeymoon, Mrs. Claus wanted to avoid looking like a newlywed. 'Santa, how can I give the appearance of a woman who's been married for years?'

'Easy, just carry the suitcases!'

***

Santa and Rudolph were discussing diets when Mrs. Sleaze interrupted.

'We are what we eat,' she advised.

'You could be right,' Santa agreed.

'That would explain why you're fast, cheap and easy!'

Hookers

By the time he delivered to the lonely hooker, Santa was pissed.

'How about you and me getting our rocks off?' He slurred as he put a cheap gift in her stocking, 'you look as if you could use a few dollars.'

'A few dollars indeed.

'Why on earth would I charge by the inch?'

***

Gypsy, the hooker was giving birth. 'Push hard,' the doctor yelled and her baby's head pushed out, 'good heavens, your baby is Asian it's got slanted eyes.'

'I'm not surprised,' she gasped, 'I do fuck Asian men.'

Gypsy pushed harder and the baby's body appeared. 'Good grief, your baby's body is black.'

'Well Doctor, I fuck black men too.'

She pushed harder and the baby's legs appeared. 'His little legs are white.'

'So, I fuck white men too.'

Doctor pulled the baby all the way out, cut the cord and slapped him on the bum.

The baby yelled.

'A perfectly healthy child but, how on earth are you going to cope with a child with slanted eyes, a black body and white legs?'

'No problem, Doc.

'I'm just relieved he doesn't bark!'

***

Fairy Floss and husband Ken were having financial problems. Fairy Floss offered to help out by hooking, short term of course! Ken drove her to a popular street and said he'd wait just around the corner in case she needed help.

A man drove up and asked, 'How much to go all the way?' Fairy Floss didn't have a clue so she ran to ask Ken.

'Tell him eighty bucks!'

'That's too much,' the man said, 'how much for a hand job?'

Again, she raced to ask Ken.

'Tell him thirty bucks.'

The client agreed and revealed the most well endowed member in the North Pole.

Fairy Floss couldn't believe her eyes. She raced back to Ken.

'Quick,' she demanded.

'You have to lend me fifty bucks!'

***

'Santa what can I get Jimmy the Jewish elf for Xmas?' Jack the elf asked.

'Why not get him a porno video that runs backwards.'

'Why?'

'Cause he'll probably like the part where the Hooker hands the money back!'

***

Santa and Stupid were having a quiet beer, when they noticed the hooker and the drug dealer making a sneaky exchange, across the street.

'Who do you suppose makes the most money?' Stupid asked.

'The hooker of course.

'She resells the same crack over and over again!'

***

Stupid the elf and Emerald the Irish elf, booked in at the North Pole Casino for a weekend of gambling and hookers. After an evening of roulette, they took the hookers up to their adjoining rooms. Emerald was so intimidated by the six-foot hooker's height, he couldn't get it up. And to ad to his depression, he had to listen to the cries of 'One, two, three huh,' coming from Stupid's room, all night long.

The next morning they met a breakfast. 'How was it with that six foot hooker?' Stupid asked.

'Fuckin' awful, I've never been so embarrassed. I just couldn't get it up.'

'You call that embarrassing?

'I couldn't even get onto the fuckin' bed!'

***

Santa delivered to the girls in a no frills, red light district. Stupid the elf eyed off the shabby ramshackle building as he waited in the sleigh. A scantily clad girl sidled up and asked, 'If he wanted a bit?'

'Why?' Asked Stupid.

'Are they tearing it down?'

***

Fairy Floss wanted to save money. Ken Floss agreed to put all his pocket change into her heart shaped piggy bank every time they made love.

Months later, he knocked it off the bedside table and it smashed to pieces. He was surprised to see handfuls of notes amongst the coins.

'Where the fuck did all these notes come from?' He asked.

'Well, Santa's not as cheap as you!'

***

The Gypsy hooker and her friend waited on the street corner. 'We can expect a busy night,' said Gypsy, 'I smell cock in the air.'

'No, that was me,' the other hooker said.

'I just burped!'

***

A sign over the door of the new Gypsy House of Ill Repute read, 'Exotic Gypsy Girls.'

Santa decided to try them.

'I'm very impressed with you,' the Gypsy hooker said after a lusty session with Santa, 'I'd like give you a freebie. Of course, you may like to rest for five minutes.'

'I'll be in that,' said Santa 'but, while I rest you'll have to bloody well hang on to my cock with both hands.'

'That's a bit inconvenient but, I suppose it's to keep your interest up while you're resting.'

'No, it's not that. I want to know where your hands are at all times.

'You see, the last time a Gypsy told me to rest, the bitch stole my wallet!'

***

Santa delivered to the high-class hooker in Japan. He decided to try her pleasures. Thru out the hour of passion, the beautiful girl kept screaming 'Fujifoo! Fujifoo!' It spurred Santa on.

A few days later, he was golfing with his friend from the North Pole Japanese restaurant. After getting a hole in one, Santa decided to impress by yelling 'Fujifoo! Fujifoo!'

'No no,' his friend shook his head.

'You've got the right hole!'

***

Ken Floss and the Gypsy hooker met at her place. 'Wanta put your finger in my pussy?' She asked

Ken obliged and she moaned, 'Put your whole hand in my pussy.'

Ken followed orders. 'Put both hands in,' she gasped.

He did and she yelled, 'Now clap your hands.'

'I can't.'

'See, didn't I tell you I had a tight pussy!'

***

Santa delivered to the tough Yukon whore-house. 'Let me give you a gift Santa,' said the grateful madam, 'just choose any girl and she's yours for free.'

'Thanks,' said Santa, trying to sound as macho as possible, 'just give me the toughest, roughest bitch you've got.'

'Then you want Randy Rusty in room 3 at the top of the stairs.' The madam handed Santa two beers and ushered him up the stairs.

Santa kicked the door open. 'I want Randy Rusty the toughest, roughest bitch in the Yukon.'

'You've found her,' a big strong naked redhead said. She bent over and grabbed her ankles.

'Hey, what makes you think I want to do it in that position?' Santa objected.

'Dickhead.

'I thought you might like to open the beers before we get started!'

***

Santa's father, Old Timer was feeling horny but, he only had ten dollars and was forced to use the services of the No Frills whorehouse. A few days later, he realised he'd caught the crabs. He stormed back to the hooker. 'Shit, Lady, you gave me the crabs.'

'Well, what the fuck did you expect for ten bucks?

'Caviar or lobster?'

***

Stupid went to the see the new hooker. She lay spread-eagled on a bed wearing only a pair of red crotch-less panties. 'Come over here, Lover,' she said in her sexiest voice.

Stupid backed right off.

'No way,' he said.

'If your snatch can do that to panties, there's no way my dick's going anywhere near it!'

The Sleaze Family

When Mrs. Ima Sleaze took a course in genealogy, she discovered she was descended from the Fluff family. Neva Fluff and his wife Hoosa Fluff were amongst the first white settlers at the North Pole. They begat six children, sons Fuller Fluff, Bumm Fluff and Deep Fluff; and daughters Giva Fluff, Oha Fluff and Loda Fluff.

Neva Fluff's brother Dum Fluff also a First Settler, moved nearby with his lovely Indian wife White Cloud Fluff and sons, Soft Fluff, Running Fluff and Beeg Fluff.

They married their cousins, Giva, Oha and Loda.

Soft Fluff's wife Giva Fluff gave birth to a son Watta Fluff and daughter Awe Fluff. Running Fluff's wife Oha Fluff produced two girls, Wishicood Fluff and Hoocaresa Fluff. And Beeg Fluff's wife Loda finally produced twins, son Chicken Fluff and daughter Pisa Fluff.

Watta Fluff married cousin Pisa Fluff and they had two boys, Dawg Fluff and Sneaky Fluff. Chicken Fluff married Wishicood Fluff and gave birth to daughters Liddle Fluff and Pussy Fluff.

Pussy Fluff married Liddle Fluff and became the proud parents of Foreva Fluff and Ima Fluff who both defied family tradition.

Foreva Fluff was lesbian and didn't marry at all.

Ima Fluff married Sucha Sleaze and became Ima Sleaze. Ima Sleaze and Sucha Sleaze have a daughter Trashette; and a son Trash.

***

Santa stopped off at the home of the Sleaze family to enquire of their wants for Xmas. 'Is your mother home?' He asked young Trash.

'She's out the back screwing the goat.'

'Santa won't bring you anything if you tell lies.'

'I'm not lying, Santa. Come out the back and I'll show you.'

Santa was shocked to see Ima Sleaze making it with the goat. 'I am absolutely disgusted. You poor child it must be so hard to live like this.'

Trash shook his head and opened his mouth.

'And cried, 'Naaaaaaaaahhhhh!'

***

'Doc, you've got to help me,' Mr. Sleaze begged, 'I often have sex with an elephant, but this time things went wrong.'

'Bend over and let me have a look at your ass,' said the shocked doctor. 'Good grief your arsehole is a foot wide.

'An elephant's dick is thin and long and couldn't have done this much damage. What happened?'

'Well this time, the bastard fingered me first!'

***

'Mrs. Sleaze, How did you get these bruises on the out side of your thighs?' Doctor asked.

'From the pressure on my legs during sex.'

'Well, I suggest you change position until they heal.'

'I can't do that Doctor.

'My dog's breath is awful!'

***

Mrs. Sleaze drank to excess at Santa's wild Xmas party. She wandered outside to get some fresh air and lay down on a bench. A lactating deer stepped awkwardly over her.

'Easy, Fellows,' she said.

'One at a time, one at a time!'

***

'How's your sex life with your husband?' Doctor asked Mrs. Sleaze.

'It's called Social Security Sex, Doctor.'

'What's Social Security Sex?'

'You get a little each month, but not near enough to live on!'

***

Mrs. Claus and Mrs. Sleaze were shopping for vegetables. 'These over sized potatoes remind me of my husband's testies,' Ima Sleaze said.

'Really, are Sucha's testicles that big?'

'No but they're that dirty!'

***

'Dad, can I have ten dollars for a blowjob?' Trash asked.

'I'm not sure.

'Are you any good?'

***

Young Trashette and her boy friend were necking on the front porch. He lent against the door with one hand and asked, 'How about a blowjob?'

'No way,' she said.

'A real quick one?'

'No. Piss off.'

'Pretty please, you know you'll love it.'

'Get lost, I said no.'

'Come on after all it is Xmas.'

The door was yanked open by young Trash. 'Dad says, either you blow him, I blow him or he'll come down stairs and blow his hand off the intercom!'

***

Mrs. Sleaze walked into Trashette's room. She held up a packet of condoms. 'I found these in your school bag. Are you sexually active?'

'Not really,' said Trashette.

'I usually just lie there!'

***

The wholesome young teacher noticed young Trash's poor marks at school. 'Is something bothering you, Trash?'

'Yes,' said Trash, 'I think I'm in love.'

'But Trash, you're only eight. Who are you in love with?'

'You Teach.'

'Oh, Trash, that's flattering but, I'm a grown up and you're a child. One day I'd like to have a husband, but I don't want a child.'

'No worries,' said the lovesick Trash.

'I'll use condoms!'

***

Mrs. Sleaze took her children to the doctor for a check up. 'Trash and Trashette both need iron supplements,' said Doctor. Mrs. Sleaze didn't like to admit she had never heard of iron supplements. She knew ball bearings were made from iron, so she put ball bearings in with their breakfast cereal.

That afternoon Trashette stormed in from school. 'Every time I pee, I piss ball bearings.'

'Don't worry, it's because I put ball bearings in your food.'

'Shit,' said Trash. That explains things.'

'Explains what?'

'Explains why I shot the dog, when I jacked off behind the barn!'

***

Mr. Sleaze was finally released from the solitary confinement wing at the North Pole prison. He was placed in a cell with another inmate.

'I have to have sex right now,' he told his cellmate, 'do you want to be the sexy wife or the dominant husband?'

'I'll be the husband,' said the frightened man.

'Good, now get you arse over here and suck your wife's dick!'

***

Mrs. Claus was helping out at school. She had been warned about Trash's bad language. 'Never allow him to answer questions,' the headperson advised.

'I'm going to write each letter of the alphabet on the board,' Mrs. Claus told the class, 'and if you can tell me a word starting with that letter, please raise your hand. We will start with the letter A.'

Trash was first to raise his hand, but Mrs. Claus asked Fairyboy, Fairy Floss's son.

'A is for apple,' Fairyboy said politely.

'Excellent Fairyboy, you're absolutely right.

'My next letter is B.' Trash's hand shot up again, but Mrs. Claus asked Mary Xmas.

'B is for butter,' Mary Xmas answered.

She went quickly thru the numbers until the letter P, when the only child to raise a hand was Trash. 'I have no choice, but to let him answer,' she anguished.

'Trash.'

'Pig!'

Mrs. Claus gasped with relief. 'Trash I'm so relieved, just the word pig?'

'Sure just a fat arse, big dick, son of a bitch, shit house, mother fuckin' pig!'

***

Mr. and Mrs. Sleaze were stranded on a small desert island. Because there was nothing else to do, they fucked day and night. Eventually all the sex took a toll on Mrs. Sleaze and she died.

Mr. Sleaze found the first month unbearable, the second month devastating and the third month horrendous. By the time the fourth month rolled around Mr. Sleaze couldn't cope any longer.

He gave in and buried her!

***

Mrs. Claus was helping out at school. Teacher left instructions to introduce multi-syllable words, such as Monday Tuesday and so forth.

'Does anyone know a multi-syllable word?' She asked.

Trash Sleaze raised his hand but, Mrs. Claus avoided him. She asked Fairyboy.

'Saturday,' he answered.

'Very good, Saturday has three syllables. It's a long word.'

'I know a longer word with four syllables,' Trash said.

Mrs. Claus couldn't think of a swear word with four syllables so she decided it was safe to go with four. 'Yes, Trash?'

'Masturbation!'

Mrs. Claus was shocked but, noticed the children weren't familiar with the word.

'I'll gloss over it and change the subject,' she thought.

'Thank you Trash, four syllables is quite a mouthful.'

'No it's not.

'Blowjob is the mouthful.

'But, it's only got two syllables!'

***

Santa was having a drink with Mr. Sleaze. 'Lady Luck shone on me yesterday, I found a whole case of whisky near the rail line,' Santa said.

'I was lucky near the rail line too,' said Mr. Sleaze, 'I found a beautiful naked girl lying there and I fucked her all day long.'

'Wow, did she give you a blowjob?'

'How could she.

'She didn't have a head!'

***

The Sleaze children, Trash and Trashette were expelled from school for swearing. Mrs Sleaze sort Santa's help. 'I can't bring myself to smack them,' she said.

'They've been swearing all their lives,' said Santa, 'and whether you like it or not you're gonna have to belt the shit out of them. It's the only way they'll learn quickly.

'And by the way, don't swear yourself and speak nicely to them.'

The next morning, Mrs. Sleaze asked Trash in the nicest way, for his choice of breakfast. 'A fuckin' cheese omelette would be nice.'

Without warning, she backhanded him hard. He slammed against the wall and slid to the floor. Petrified and in shock Trash returned to his chair and sat quietly.

'That went well,' she thought. She turned to Trashette. 'Now, what would my darling daughter like for breakfast?'

'Well, there's no way in friggin' hell, I'm gonna ask for a fuckin' cheese omelette!'

***

Mr. Sleaze woke during the night to find his most cherished possession hard, for the first time in years. He shook his wife awake. 'What do you think we should do with this?' He cried with excitement.

'Shit Sucha, how the hell would I know?

'But, seeing you've got the wrinkles out it's a good time to think about washing it!'

***

The Sleaze family's carpet was badly stained by the dog. 'How can I choose a colour that won't show dog shit stains?' Mrs. Sleaze asked her husband.

'Easy.'

He cut a stained piece from the carpet and handed it to her.

'Just ask the fuckin' carpet specialist to match this!'

***

Mrs. Sleaze became the new Personnel Manager at the timber mill. A blind man applied for a position in quality control. 'I can identify any timber in the world, just by smell,' he said.

Mrs. Sleaze placed a sample of walnut on the table. 'Walnut,' he responded, 'excellent sample, strong enough for Santa's sleigh.'

She replaced the walnut with cedar. 'Cedar but a mediocre sample, not suitable for fine furniture.'

Next, she tried pine. 'Pine, a good piece but, should only be used in low cost furniture.'

On impulse, Mrs. Sleaze lifted her skirt and put her crotch right in his face. 'I'm not sure,' he said, 'can you turn it around?'

She turned around and put her arsehole right in front of his face and pulled her cheeks apart.

'Of course, it's the shit house door off a tuna boat!'

***

Mrs. Sleaze and her mother were nymphomaniacs. They had sex with anyone and everyone. When Mrs. Sleaze first met her future husband, she told him she was a virgin. 'Mother, what can I do on my wedding night to make my pussy tight?'

'Just put an apple in before sex and he'll be none the wiser.'

The honeymoon went well, until Mrs. Sleaze left the apple on the wash- basin.

Mr. Sleaze ate the apple.

She called her mother. 'I'm worried he may be poisoned, what if the apple kills him?'

'Don't worry Dear.

'Your father lived after he ate the sugar-melon I left on the basin during our honeymoon!'

***

Mrs. Claus walked her poodle Angel Face past the Sleaze family home. Mr. Sleaze staggered down the steps and stared at Angel Face. 'Where did ya get the fat arsed pig?' He slurred.

'She's not a pig you drunken bum, she is a pedigreed French Poodle.'

'Shut ya face.

'I was talking to the poodle!'

***

Mrs. Sleaze was enjoying a coffee break at the toy factory. Santa walked over and sat next to her. 'Can I smell your cunt?' He asked

'No, you arrogant prick, you can't smell my cunt.'

Santa looked puzzled.

'Oh, well. It must be your feet!'

***

Mr. and Mrs. Sleaze were tossing peanuts in the air and catching them in their mouths. Mr. Sleaze accidentally caught one in his ear. When he tried to get if out it went further in.

Trashette arrived home with her new boyfriend. 'Let me help,' he said, 'I'm studying medicine. I'll just put two fingers up your nostrils and ask you to blow hard.'

The nut shot out of the ear and across the room. The Sleazes were most impressed.

When he left, Mrs. Sleaze asked, 'Do you think he's fucking our daughter?'

'I know for sure he is.'

'How do you know?'

'Cos he had his fingers up my nose, Remember?'

***

Mrs. Sleaze opened a sleazy whorehouse. On the first morning, the queue reached around the block. Stupid the elf was her last client. 'I've never eaten a girl out before and I want to do it now.'

Mrs. Sleaze was a little short on girls, so she hastily grabbed her Master at Arms, a deadly, leather clad, whip-wheeling lesbian.

'It's his first time, he won't know the difference,' Mrs. Sleaze said as she charged Stupid three times the going rate.

Stupid stuck his tongue in the lesbian's black abyss and got a piece of carrot in his mouth. As this was his first time, he thought it could be the norm, so he continued on. He almost swallowed a piece off a corncob, followed by half a sausage and a piece of meat.

'Excuse me Miss,' he said as he came up with more meat, 'I hope you're not sick.'

'Not me,' she cackled.

'But, the guy before you was!'

***

Trashette asked her father if she could go to a Xmas party.

'No. Not unless you suck my dick first.'

'I hate sucking your dick Pa, please can I go?'

'If you suck my dick, not only will I let you go but, I'll let you stay as late as you like.'

Trashette gave in and decided to get it over and done with. 'Yuk, Pa! Your dick tastes like shit.'

'Of course.

'Your brother wanted to borrow the car!'

***

Trash and Fairyboy were picked up by the cops for smoking pot. They appeared before a sweet young magistrate. 'I'm going to take into account your young ages and your remorse. You are evidently ashamed and sorry for your actions. Therefore I will give you a week to go out amongst the young drug takers in our community and persuade them to give up drugs.

'We will meet back here at 10am Monday and based on your success, I will make a decision to either lock you up, or give you a caution.'

A week passed and Trash and Fairyboy fronted court again.

'I spoke to twenty classes of high school students over five days,' Fairyboy declared, 'and I persuaded 50% of drug taking students to sign a form pledging to give up drugs forever.'

'That's amazing,' said the magistrate, 'how did you manage that?'

'Well, Trash and I stayed up all night devising a plan. We decided to draw a large and a small circle on the blackboard and tell kids that the large circle represents your brain before taking drugs and the small circle represents your brain after taking drugs. They sure got the message.'

'That's admirable. I must congratulate you.

'And how did you go Trash?'

Trash looked confused. 'I requested and got permission to address three high school assemblies. That's about 6,000 students and I got 100% of them to sign the note promising to give up drugs forever.'

'Outstanding,' cried Your Honour, 'you got 6,000 people to give up drugs just by using the small and large circle method?'

'Yes but, I got muddled up, I drew the two circles and said, "the small circle represents your arsehole before prison.

'And the large circle represents your arsehole after prison!"

***

Trash grew up and took Cecil as his lover. One day Trash said, 'Cecil, there seems to be something up my arse, can you check it out?'

Cecil stuck his hand where the sun don't shine and felt around as best he could. 'Can't find anything!'

'Lube your hand up and try again. Please.'

Cecil followed instructions and this time he scored. 'Shit, there's a Rolex watch stuck up your arse.'

Trash burst into song.

'Happy birthday to you, happy birthday to you!'

***

Trashette was working as a child hooker. The North Pole police raided the brothel and lined the hookers up along the footpath.

'Trashette, why are you waiting in line with all these young girls?' Mrs. Claus asked.

'The police are giving out free oranges,' she lied.

'Why would anyone want free oranges?'

'They're great to suck on.'

'Your right, I haven't sucked oranges for ages.' Mrs. Claus reminisced as she went to the end of the line.

The police officer questioned each girl as he made his way down the line. When he got to Mrs. Claus, he couldn't believe his eyes.

'How on earth do you do it at your age?' He asked.

'Oh it's not as hard as you think Officer.

'I just remove my dentures and suck 'em dry!'

***

Although Trashette was a minor she appeared in a porno movie, wearing a long black wig and speaking with a phoney French accent. The movie was hard-core with sado-masochism, oral sex, anal sex, group sex and animal sex. Trashette starred in a disgusting scene being serviced by a large dog.

When the movie opened at the North Pole, she sat in the back row of the porno theatre wearing dark glasses and a trench coat.

Santa slunk into the seat next to her. He also wore dark glasses and a trench coat. Although they were incognito, they recognised each other.

Santa panicked. 'I'm only here to hear the music, a friend of mine wrote the score.'

Trashette also panicked.

'And I'm only here to see your dog!'

***

Trashette was visiting her grandparents. 'Grandpa, Grannie say's you can show me a magic trick. Can you Grandpa, please?'

'Sure can. Just come sit on my lap.'

Trashette sat on his lap. 'Can you feel my finger poking up your snatch?'

'Sure can, Grandpa.'

'Well, look.

'No hands!'

***

Trashette grew up and opened a new bar. She called it 'Trashette's Legs.' Mr. Sleaze had a hangover and turned up early to wait for the bar to open.

The diligent police officer watched him with suspicion. 'Why the hell are you loitering?'

'I'm waiting for Trashette's Legs to open so I can get a drink!'

***

Mrs. Sleaze ran into Santa at the hospital donation centre. 'I'm here to donate blood,' she announced, 'they pay $5.'

'Gee, that's not much. I'm here to donate sperm, they pay $50.'

'Wow, that's a lot, thanks for telling me Santa.'

The next week, Santa noticed Mrs. Sleaze waiting for the donation centre to open. 'Here to donate blood again?' He asked.

Mrs. Sleaze shook her head.

'No?' Santa asked again.

Mrs. Sleaze shook her head again. She kept her mouth shut and murmured, 'Na uh Na uh!'

***

Mr. Sleaze found a naked elf tied to a tree. 'Jesus Jack, what happened to you?'

'I gave a ride to a lady hitchhiker and she pulled a gun on me. She took my wallet and clothes, tied me up then drove off in my car. I guess this isn't my day!'

Mr. Sleaze looked at the shivering naked elf and unzipped his pants.

'I reckon you're right Jack.

'I reckon you're right!'

***

Trashette grew up. Her wedding day dawned. She arrived at church wearing a see-thru gown and no underwear. Mary Xmas was shocked. 'Santa, Is there a reason the bride isn't wearing knickers?'

'Yes and a very good reason.

'It keeps the flies off the cake!'

***

Mr. Sleaze drove over one of Santa's reindeer and killed it. He decided to barbeque it for dinner. Not wanting to upset Trashette with the sight of a dead deer, he cut it into small pieces.

'These steaks taste funny,' Trash remarked. 'Dad, what are we eating?'

'I'll tell you later.'

'Tell us now Dad. What are we eating?'

Trash kept it up until the meal was finished. 'Okay, Trash, I'll give you a hint. What does your mother call me, sometimes?'

'Shit,' yelled Trashette.

'We've eaten arsehole!'

Black black black

Sometimes we forget the true meaning of Xmas,' Santa said to the elves, 'we also forget Jesus was black.'

'What makes you say that?'

'Well, he called everybody Brother and he never got a fair trial!'

***

'Santa, what's an IQ test?' the young Aboriginal boy asked.

'Well, it's a measure of your intellect. If your IQ is above 120 it means you're highly intelligent. If it's around 100 you are of average intelligence and if it's below 50 you're completely stupid. So stupid in fact, you'd find it hard to even do your shoe laces up.'

'Thanks Santa, now I know why most white men wear thongs!'

***

Santa and Emerald the Irish elf delivered toys to Australia. 'Santa, did you know I once spent time in Australia?' Emerald asked.

'Is that so, how was it?'

'The people were so friendly. Strangers invited me to share their food. They entertained me and insisted on sharing their homes. I toured all six states and it never cost me a fuckin' cent.'

'Shit,' said Santa, 'Aussies must be the most hospitable people in the whole friggin' world.'

'Sure are.

'It's just those white bastards you've got to watch!'

***

'I think cannibals are the most trusting people in the world,' Santa said to Rudolph.

'Why?'

'Well, they give each other blowjobs don't they?'

***

'Santa, the black bride is dressed from head to toe in snowy white.'

'Yes, she's wearing white as a symbol of chastity and purity. It means she's waited to be married before indulging in sex.'

'Santa, why is the groom wearing black?'

***

Jack the black elf borrowed Santa's sleigh. 'I had a terrible time, Santa. A big white bird crapped all over the seats.'

'Shit, that's disgusting. Don't take her out again!'

***

Mrs. Claus and the Xmas Fairy were flying with North Pole Air. Suddenly the captain made an announcement. 'Prepare for an emergency landing!'

'Quick,' Mrs. Claus yelled to the Xmas Fairy, 'take off your top and bra.'

'Good thinking, Mrs. Claus and you must put all your jewellery on.'

'Why?' A black lady asked.

'Well,' said Mrs. Claus, 'when they come to rescue us they'll think I'm rich, so they'll probably rescue me first.'

'And, when they see my irresistible tits,' said The Xmas Fairy, 'they'll rescue me with her.'

'That makes sense,' said the black lady, as she quickly got naked from the waist down.

'Why are you showing your snatch?' Mrs. Claus and the Xmas Fairy chorused together.

'Well, I've just remembered the first thing rescuers look for.

'It's the black box!'

***

Stupid, the elf had a new girlfriend. She insisted he have her name Winny tattooed on his dick. When his dick was erect it spelt 'Winny' and when it was limp it spelled 'Wy.'

They visited the North Pole nudist colony. Stupid noticed a black man with 'Wy' also tattooed on his dick. 'Can I ask if your dick says Winny when it's erect?' Stupid asked.

'No, of course it doesn't say Winny.

'It says 'welcome to the North Pole, have a fabulous day and enjoy your stay!"

Stupid

Santa saw Stupid leave the toy factory, carrying a roll of duct tape. 'Where you going with the duct tape?'

'I've taken up hunting, I'm gonna catch ducks.'

'Stupid, you can't catch ducks with duct tape.'

'Well, I'm as sure as shit gonna try.'

Later, Santa saw Stupid walking home dragging a flock of ducks behind him.

The next afternoon Stupid left the toy factory carrying a roll of chicken wire. 'Where are you going with the chicken wire, Stupid?'

'To catch chickens of course.'

'You can't catch chickens with chicken wire.'

'Bet your aunt's fanny I can.'

Sure enough, Stupid walked past later dragging about eight chickens.

The next day, Stupid left work carrying what looked like a small branch. 'What's that?' Santa asked.

'Pussy willow.'

'No shit. Hold on a minute.

'I'll be right with you!'

***

'I must deliver toys to San Jose,' Santa said to Stupid, 'do you know the quickest way?'

'Are you flying or driving?'

'Flying the friggin' sleigh of course.'

'Yeah well, that's probably the quickest way!'

***

Santa and Stupid the elf were pissed. They went to the circus to see the macho Lady Lion Tamer. She put a biscuit between her teeth and a snarling lion opened his massive jaws and took the biscuit from her.

The crowd went wild and when the applause died down Stupid called out, 'I could do that and I could do a better friggin' job.'

'Well, you'd better come up here and show us.'

'And I will.

'Just as soon, as you get those fuckin' lions out of the cage!'

***

'Do you know anything about pigs?' Stupid asked Santa.

'Sure do.'

'Well, how can you tell if they're pregnant? My pigs are all female and their not getting pregnant.'

'Of course your pigs aren't pregnant. To become pregnant they have to have a male fucking them. Do you understand?'

'Yeah, I think so.' Stupid thought for a moment.

'So, if a male fucks them, how can I tell if they're pregnant?'

'If they're standing up the morning after a male fucks them, they're not pregnant. But, if they're rolling around in the mud, they are pregnant.'

The next evening, Stupid drove the pigs into the orange orchard and fucked them, one by one. The next morning, he was disappointed to find them all standing.

This routine continued for a week. Stupid was exhausted. On the seventh day he was too tired to check on his pigs. He slept all day.

Santa called in during the afternoon. Stupid asked Santa to look out the window. 'Just tell me what the pigs are doing,' he asked.

'Well, they're all standing up in the back of the truck and one of them is leaning on the horn!'

***

Mrs. Claus was teaching an awareness course for adults. On the first night she was shocked to find the word PENIS written on the white board.

Stupid was the only student wearing a big grin.

She decided he was guilty, ignored the whole thing and rubbed the offensive word off.

Each night the word appeared in slightly larger letters. Each night she rubbed it away.

The final night of the course arrived and Mrs. Claus walked in, fully expecting to be greeted by the word again, but instead found a message.

'BE AWARE THE MORE YOU RUB THE BIGGER IT GETS!'

***

'A frog spoke to me and told me to drive across the bridge on my way home,' Stupid told North Pole Judge, 'I did drive across the bridge and I was the millionth person to do so. That's how I won an all expenses paid, stay at the luxury hotel.'

'Go on.'

'I took the frog with me and it demanded I kiss it. I didn't want to, but I felt obligated.'

'Go on.'

'Well, I kissed the frog and it turned into a beautiful thirteen year old girl.

'And that's the only reason I came to be holed up in the hotel room, with a thirteen year old girl your Honour!'

***

Stupid the elf answered the following ad. 'If you love your country more than anything and would like to earn one million bucks per year, apply to the FBI.'

Stupid was third in line to be interviewed. The recruitment officer handed the first man a gun and said. 'Your wife is in the next room. To pass the first test, you must go in and kill her.'

The man got up in disgust and left.

He passed the gun to the second man and gave him the same instructions. Thru the two-way mirror Stupid watched the man raise his gun to his wife's head then change his mind.

'I just can't do it,' he cried. He grabbed her hand and left.

'You're next,' said the recruitment officer. Stupid walked in to where his wife was waiting.

Three gunshots rang out. A loud scuffling noise followed.

Stupid came back in the room and handed the gun to the officer. 'I'm really pissed off,' he said, 'how in the hell did you expect me to kill her with friggen blanks in the gun?

'I had to fuckin' well strangle her!'

***

Three elves, Stupid, Emerald and Jack were stuck on an island. They found a magic lamp. When they rubbed it a Genie popped out and granted them one wish each.

Jack wished to be a third smarter, so he could get off the island. He suddenly realised the mainland was quite close and swam off the island.

Emerald wished to be 50% smarter so he could get off the island. He noticed a rowboat washed up on the sand, so he jumped in and rowed to the mainland.

Stupid wished to be 100% smarter, so he could get off the island.

He turned into a woman and walked across the bridge!

***

Stupid's wife was lying in bed, thinking sensuous thoughts. Stupid was reading a book.

Suddenly he reached over and stroked her pussy until she groaned and became quite moist. She couldn't believe her luck. She sat up and shed her nightgown.

'What are you doing?' Stupid asked.

'I'm getting ready for sex of course, you just stroked my pussy.'

'Oh that!

'I was just wetting my fingers, so I could turn the pages!'

***

To save on rent, Santa moved part of the toy factory to the isolated inland. 'The nearest women are miles away in town,' Santa said, 'so we'll keep a pet camel close by, in case any of us gets lonely.'

After a few weeks Stupid felt lonely, so he brought the camel around to the back of his hut. He stood on a chair and managed to have sex with it.

As he walked around his hut and zipped up his pants, he was stunned to see Santa and the elves staring in shock.

'What's wrong? Isn't that what the camel's for?'

'Shit, no.' Said Santa.

'We use the camel to ride into town!'

***

'My wife is so dumb,' Santa complained to the elves, 'she paid a fortune for a size eight designer bikini, when she needs one big enough to fit an elephant.'

'What about my wife?' Emerald joined in, 'she's gone and got a microwave oven and we don't even have electricity.'

'Mine's even dumber than both of yours,' Stupid said, 'she's got condoms in her wallet.

'And she doesn't even have a dick!'

***

Because Santa moved a section of his toy factory to the isolated inland, he decided to build a barrel for the boys. 'When you guys get horny, you can just pump away in the barrel,' he said.

After a week Stupid decided he needed to visit the barrel. He unzipped his pants and slid his cock in the hole. The barrel took on an amazing sucking effect. It was so good Stupid waited about five minutes, then went back for more.

'That barrel is unbelievable,' he said to Santa, 'best fuck I ever had, think I'll book in daily.'

'You can't,' said Santa, 'you can only have it Monday to Saturday. You can't use it on Sunday.'

'Is that because it's the Sabbath?'

'No, it's because on Sunday, it's your turn inside the barrel!'

***

Stupid's wife was fed up with him throwing up all over himself during his drunken binges. She made him promise not to drink. Of course he broke his promise, drank too much and threw up all down his new jacket.

'Make sure you have a twenty dollar note in your hand, when you walk thru the front door,' Santa said.

'Why?'

'Cause you can tell her a drunk gave you twenty dollars for dry cleaning, after he threw up all over you.'

Stupid crept thru the door to find his wife waiting. He was tanked. 'You've thrown up again all down your new shirt and pants, haven't you? And why are you hanging onto that twenty dollar note?'

'Cause the drunk who threw up over me, gave it to me for dry-cleaning, that's why.'

'Well, that is good news. What's the other twenty dollars for?'

'That's from the guy who shit in my pants!'

***

Santa arrived back at the North Pole just in time for a double funeral. Two hearses lead the funeral procession for Stupid's wife and his mother-in-law. Stupid walked behind, followed by his dog and almost every man in the district.

'What happened?' Santa asked as he respectfully joined the procession.

'Well, my dog bit my wife and she fell down dead,' said Stupid, 'and then it bit my mother-in-law and she fell dead.'

'Shit, I'm sorry Stupid.'

Santa was thoughtful as he walked beside his friend. 'Stupid can I borrow your dog?'

'Sure can.

'But, you'll just have to get in line behind the rest of the men!'

***

Santa and Stupid were having a quiet beer on the back porch. 'Is your bum asleep?' asked Stupid.

'No. Why?'

'I just heard it snoring!'

***

Stupid walked into the men's room and found a man without arms standing at the urinal. 'Could you please help me unzip my pants and lifting my dick out?' He asked.

Stupid was horrified, but didn't know how he could refuse. He unzipped the stranger's pants and pulled his dick out. The guy urinated and asked Stupid to push it back and zip his pants up again.

Stupid complied, but was horrified at the sight of the green mouldy dick. 'What the hell's wrong with it?' He asked.

'Wouldn't have a clue,' said the guy as he pulled his arms out of his sleeves.

'But, I sure as hell won't touch it!'

***

Stupid had finally gotten thru medical school. The Dean looked down his nose and said, 'Because it has taken you thirty years and many failures, we need to observe you with a patient, prior to issuing your certificate of practice.'

The distinguished members of the board, watched thru a two-way mirror. 'I have a problem with bed-wetting, Doctor,' the voluptuous patient said, 'the problem only occurs during the night.'

Stupid instructed her to take her clothes off and stand on her head, with legs apart, facing the mirror. When she was ready, he rested his chin between her legs and looked in the mirror.

'Ah ha,' he said and walked back to his desk. He told the woman to get dressed. 'You should be fine providing you don't drink any liquid after six thirty at night!'

The woman left and the members of the board filed in. 'Your diagnosis was excellent! But, why did you have the patient get naked stand on her head in front of the mirror?'

'Oh, that!

'I just wanted to see how I would look with a beard!'

***

Santa went with Stupid to the sperm bank, Stupid came out with raised eyebrows. 'How come you look surprised?' Santa asked.

'I'm surprised the nurse thanked me for coming!'

***

Santa and Stupid were having a beer at the bar. Santa was fed up with people stealing his drink when he went to the bathroom, so he put a sign on his beer saying, 'I spat in this beer.'

While he was away, Stupid put up another sign.

'So did I!'

***

The North Pole psychologist decided to run a sex therapy class for men. At the first session, he asked for a show of hands for men who had sex once a day. A few hands were raised.

He then asked for a show of hands for those who had sex once a week. More hands went up.

And finally he asked for hands to show those who had sex once a month. The majority of hands were raised.

Doctor noticed that although Stupid grinned thru the whole procedure, he didn't raise a hand at all. 'Stupid, do you mind telling us how often you have sex?'

'Once a year, Doc.'

'Only once a year, how come you're so happy about it?'

'Well, Doc.

'Tonight's the night!'

***

The North Pole School of Medicine gave Stupid one more chance to get his certificate of practice. The members of the board watch thru the two way mirror as his first patient walked in. 'Doctor, my husband is a compulsive gambler and I have to hide money from him. He knows all my hiding places, so in desperation I stuck our last five hundred dollars up my snatch. And now, I can't get it out.'

'No problem. Just take your panties off, lie down and place your legs in these stirrups.'

Stupid donned his rubber gloves. 'Just one question before I go in!

'Am I looking for notes or loose change?'

***

Stupid examined his next patient. 'I've got good news and I've got bad news.'

'Give me the bad news first, Doc.'

'You've got one week to live.'

'Jesus Doc, that's terrible. How can there be good news?'

'Well, did you notice my gorgeous new receptionist?'

'Yeah.'

'Well, I'm screwing the arse off her!'

***

The desperate husband rushed his wife to Stupid's clinic. 'Quick Doc, a wasp has flown into my wife's snatch,' he cried.

'This emergency is your last chance,' the Dean of medicine said to Stupid as he ushered his colleagues out to the two-way mirror.

Stupid examined the lady and turned to her husband. 'The wasp is too far in to take with forceps. How about we put some honey on your penis and you can gently thrust your penis it in and out; and maybe entice the little bugger out.'

The husband agreed, but worried so much about getting stung, he couldn't get it up. 'I could give it a try,' said Stupid 'but, only if you both agree.'

Under the circumstances, they both agreed.

Stupid slapped honey on his penis and climbed aboard. He went in and out and waited a few seconds. Nothing happened.

Again, in and out and wait a few seconds.

Stupid suddenly quickened his pace.

'What the hell is happening here?' The husband yelled.

'Change of plans.

'I'm gonna drown the little basted!'

***

Stupid gave his first lecture at medical school. His subject was Observation. 'A good doctor must be one hundred percent observant to the five senses,' he said, 'touch, sight, sound, smell and taste.'

He held up a jar of yellow liquid. 'This is urine,' he dipped a finger into the urine and put his finger in his mouth.

'Did you observe my actions fully?' He asked. The class nodded in disgust.

'To be good students, you must follow my actions.'

'Oh, Yuk!' One by one, the students passed the jar around, dipped a finger in and then put it in their mouths.

'From this day forth,' Stupid told the surly class, 'you will be one hundred percent observant of all things.'

'How the fuck does that teach us to be observant?' An angry student yelled.

'Sir, if you were observant, you would have noticed that I put my middle finger in the jar. You would also have noticed the finger I put in my mouth.

'It was my trigger finger!'

***

Stupid took his pet wombat to the bar. While he ordered a drink, the wombat ran riot and ate a few olives, some maraschino cherries and a handful of peanuts. He then raced to the pool table, picked up a cue ball and swallowed it.

'Sorry Barman,' Stupid said, 'I'll pay for everything.'

The next day, Stupid brought his wombat back again. While he ordered a drink, the wombat stuck an olive up his bum, pulled it out and ate it. He did the same thing with a maraschino cherry.

'Oh yuk,' said the barman, 'did you see what your wombat just did?'

'Yeah he's just being careful.

'Ever since he ate that cue ball, he measures everything first!'

***

'Santa, I know what an Aussie is,' Stupid said, 'and I know what Americans, Japanese, Chinese, Russians and Brits are. But what exactly is a Yankee?'

'It's the same as a quickie.

'Only you do it yourself!'

***

As Stupid walked to town, he heard a girl crying. He looked over the fence and saw a legless and armless girl, crying beside a pool. 'What's wrong?'

'Everyone avoids me. I've never had a hug in my life.'

'There, there. I'll jump the fence and give you my very best hug.'

As he hugged the girl, he realised she had the world's worst case of body odour. 'I'm out of here,' he thought and jumped the fence; and went on his way.

On his way back from town, he heard the girl crying again. 'What's wrong, now?'

'I have only a few days to live and I've never even been kissed.'

'This is the hardest thing I'll ever do,' Stupid thought. He climbed the fence and gave her a big sloppy kiss then realised she had a shocking case of bad breath. 'I'm out of here for good,' he thought, but the girl cried loudly.

'I've never been fucked in my life.'

Stupid picked her up and threw her out into the middle of the pool.

'Well, now you're well and truly fucked!'

***

Stupid was working part time at the supermarket. A lady put her basket of goods on the check out counter. 'One small packet of washing powder, one serving of pasta, four single serves of yoghurt and one packet of mixed, frozen vegetables. 'You are single and you also live alone!' Stupid announced.

'That's amazing,' the woman cried, 'are you psychic or can you tell that from my purchase?'

'Neither. You stink and you're frighteningly ugly.

'So of course you're single and of course, you live alone!'

***

'Do you know how to turn a fox into an elephant, Santa?' Stupid asked.

'Of course.'

'How?'

'Marry her!'

***

'Are you sure you're watching your protein levels since you became vegetarian?' Santa asked Stupid.

'Sure am, I et six eggs for breakfast.'

'I think you mean ate!'

'Could be, I'm not real good at numbers so I could have et eight eggs for breakfast!'

***

The tough police officer pulled Stupid over for speeding. 'You were way over the speed limit,' she shouted as she brushed the flies away, 'I'm going to give you a ticket, if these bloody flies will leave me alone.'

'They're Arsehole flies,' said Stupid, 'they circle cattle and horses' arseholes or any arsehole they can find.'

'I don't like your tone. Are you trying to infer I'm an arsehole?'

'No not me.

'But you can't fool them flies!'

***

Santa and Stupid delivered toys to the Sahara desert. Stupid decided to go home by camel. Half way across the lonely desert he became as horny as hell. He decided to have sex with the camel, but the beast took off. Hours later he caught up with it and continued his ride.

The next day he again tried to fuck the camel and again, it took off. He eventually found it making friends with three beautiful blondes in a broken down jeep.

'If you can fix out jeep, we'll do anything you want,' the beautiful blondes said.

Stupid fixed the car and the girls were thrilled. 'Thank you, now we're all yours, we'll do whatever you want.'

The girls began to strip. Stupid thought hard for a moment.

'I know, could you please hold my camel!'

***

'When I was about sixteen, I could bend my hard on with one hand,' Stupid said to the Irish barman, 'and when I was twenty one, I could bend it about ten degrees!'

'So?'

'Well, when I turned twenty-five I could bend it about twenty degrees. And now I'm gonna be thirty I can almost bend it in half!'

The barman was sick of listening. 'What the fuck's your point?'

'Well, I'm just wondering how much stronger I can get!'

***

Stupid was as drunk as a skunk. He was trying to stand upright on the street corner. The nasty police officer came along. 'What are you waiting for?' She demanded.

'The world turns around every twenty-four hours,' Stupid slurred, 'So my house should be here any moment now.'

'Why the hell would you say that?'

'Cause, my neighbour just went by!'

***

Stupid didn't know what to wear to Santa's fancy dress party. After a lot of thought, he arrived wearing just a pair of jeans.

'What the fuck are you supposed to be?' Santa asked.

'I'm a premature ejaculation, of course.

'I've just "come in my pants!"

***

'Where's Stupid the elf?' Santa asked.

'Gone to see his doctor, seems he goes to the toilet every morning, rain hail or shine, at six thirty.'

'Well what's wrong with that? At least he's regular.'

'Yeah but, Stupid doesn't wake up until seven!'

***

Mrs. Claus was watching a fax come thru. 'This one's either from Stupid or Fairy Floss,' she said.

'What makes you say that?' Santa asked.

'It's got a stamp on it!'

***

Stupid and Santa needed a drink. A sign over the bar said

12 months free beer to anyone who can:

1. Drink a full bottle of Chilly tequila straight down.

2. Remove the sore tooth from our crocodile out the back.

3. Give Buxom Beryl the barmaid her first orgasm.

'I could do that,' Stupid said, 'give me a bottle of chilly tequila!' Stupid drank it down and coughed and spluttered. Tears ran down his face. As the room swam around, he staggered out the back and jumped in with the crocodile.

Santa and the other patrons froze as they listened to the sounds of ferocious roaring and splashing. It went on for twenty minutes, before there was a deathly silence.

Stupid staggered back into the bar with his clothing ripped to shreds and blood streaming from his wounds. Although he was deathly white and shaking, he finally managed to speak.

'Now, where the fuck's that barmaid with the sore tooth?'

***

Stupid's wife came home early and was shocked to find him fucking the daylights out of Fairy Floss.

'What in the hell are you two doing?' She yelled.

Stupid rolled his eyes at Fairy Floss.

'And people think I'm stupid!'

***

Stupid and Emerald were pissed and complaining loudly to Santa. Seems he had never taken them for a 'real ride' in the sleigh.

'Alright, if you shut up and promise not to say one word until we're back on the ground I'll take you up.

'If you utter one friggin' word before we land, you will work a whole week without pay. Agreed?'

'Agreed.'

The sleigh took off and after a few touch-and-go's Santa put the sleigh thru dives, climbs, spins and loop-de-loops.

'I'm proud of you,' Santa said as they landed, 'not one word from either of you!'

'Of course not, you prick!' Sobbed Stupid. 'When Emerald fell out at the first dive, I fuckin' froze with fright. You arsehole!

'Of course I couldn't talk!'

***

Santa and Stupid the elf were leaving the bar when they noticed a drunk watching Santa's dog Wonder lick his balls.

'Wish I could do that,' the drunk slurred.

'Well if I were you,' Stupid remarked, 'I'd get to know the dog first.

'Just, to be on the safe-side!'

***

Stupid had far too much to drink at the bar, before he realised he needed to go to the bathroom. He staggered thru the door with his bursting prick in his hand and was confronted by Mrs. Claus sitting on the can.

'You're in the wrong toilet, this is for ladies,' she yelled.

He waved his dick at her and slurred.

'So is this, so is this!'

***

It was closing time at the bar and the diligent police officer waited to catch drink drivers. Stupid staggered out, tripped over and fell into Santa's sleigh. He then fumbled around trying to find the keys.

While this was going on, everyone left the bar and drove home.

The police officer waited until Stupid finally started the sleigh and began to pull away. She pounced with her breathalyser kit.

The reading showed a zero alcohol reading.

'How can this be?' She yelled. 'You're travelling alone so you're evidently not the fucking designated driver.'

'Of course, I'm not.

'I'm the fuckin' designated decoy!'

***

Santa and Stupid watched the Koala with a baby on her back sleeping peacefully in a tree.

'Stupid, I wonder why Koalas carry babies on their backs?' Santa pondered.

'Probably beats trying to push a baby carriage up a tree!'

***

'Stupid, where can I find a hooker?' The koala asked.

'Let me introduce you to my favourite hooker and I guarantee you'll have the best sex ever.'

Stupid was right, Koala was ecstatic until the hooker asked for money. He appeared confused. Stupid pulled out his pocket dictionary and showed Koala the definition of hooker. 'It says **Hooker: Has sex for money**.'

Koala took the dictionary from Stupid and opened it at the word Koala. 'It says **Koala: Eats bush and leaves**!'

***

Santa and Stupid took Koala to their favourite bar. Koala got pissed and passed out on the floor. 'Pick that fuckin' animal up,' the barman screamed, 'you can't leave that lyin' on the floor.'

'Dickhead,' Stupid yelled back, 'that's not a lion.

'It's a koala!'

***

Stupid was the smallest of all the elves. He entered the lift to be confronted with the tallest and widest man he had ever seen. 'You're the biggest person I've ever seen,' he said.

'I'm seven foot tall I have a twelve inch dick and my name is Turner Brown.'

Stupid fainted and the man brought him back to consciousness. 'I didn't mean to scare you, but you passed out as soon as I mentioned my name, Turner Brown.'

'Oh, I'm sorry I thought you said, 'turn around!'

***

Santa trained his dog Wonder, to walk on water. When he was ready to show Stupid, Santa threw a stick out in the middle of the lake. Wonder ran across the water, picked up the stick and carried it back.

'Well, what do you think of that?' Santa asked.

Stupid thought for a moment before answering.

'I think that stupid dog of yours can't fuckin' swim!'

***

Santa was minding Mrs. Claus's toy poodle Angel Face while she was in the beauty parlour. He joined Stupid at the bar. Stupid was so drunk, he threw up all over Angel Face and left her in a pool of chunder on the floor.

'Look what you've done,' Santa yelled.

'Shit, that's the last time I drink green ginger wine.

'I don't remember eating dog!'

***

The Elves and the reindeer gathered around Santa's sick bed. He desperately needed a kidney transplant.

'Are you an organ donor?' Rudolph asked Stupid the elf.

'I'm not sure. I once gave a clapped out key board to the Old Folks Home!'

***

Sister Slosh requested an inscription on her tombstone: 'Born a virgin, lived a virgin, died a virgin.'

The undertaker gave the job to his latest helper, Stupid the elf. Stupid decided the inscription was too long. He kept it simple.

'Here lies Sister Slosh - Returned unopened!'

***

Santa and Stupid crashed the sleigh in the jungle. They were captured by a hostile tribe. 'Death or fooka?' The chief demanded.

Santa didn't have a clue what fooka was but, it sounded better than death so he opted for fooka. The tribe went into a frenzy of screaming and dancing.

When they came to a sudden stop, the chief ripped off Santa's pants and fucked him in the arse.

Stupid was horrified and when the chief asked him, 'Death or fooka?' He decided to be honourable and take death.

The tribe danced and screamed for three days. When they finally stopped the chief screamed.

'Death by fooka, death by fooka!'

***

While Mrs. Claus was eating chicken, she began to choke on a bone. Emerald, the Irish elf immediately pulled his pants down and bent over and put his bum under her face. Stupid began licking his bum.

Mrs. Claus was appalled. She threw up, chicken bone and all.

Emerald pulled his pants up and shook hands with Stupid.

'You're right, Stupid.

'That rear end lick works every time!'

***

The Dean of the University of the North Pole laid down the law to new students. 'The female dormitory is out of bounds to all male students and the male dormitory is out of bounds to all female students.

'Anyone breaking the rules will be fined $50. If caught breaking the rules a second time $100, a third time will cost you $150.'

Stupid waved his hand in the air. 'Can I ask a question?'

'Of course.'

'Can I get a season pass?'

***

Santa and the elves were adding a few stories to the toy factory. While working on the top floor, Santa decided he needed a handsaw in a hurry. He yelled to Stupid but, Stupid couldn't hear. So Santa pointed to his eye, indicating 'I,' Then pointed to his knee, indicating 'need.' He then moved his hand back and forward, as if using a handsaw.

Stupid nodded his head, indicating he got the message but, then unzipped his pants and began having a wank.

Santa couldn't believe his eyes. He climbed all the way back down to the ground.

'What the fuck are you doing? I was trying to tell you I needed a handsaw.'

'Yeah, I know that.

'And I was trying to tell you I'm coming!'

***

'Have you heard the joke about the two whales?' Stupid the elf asked Santa.

'No.'

'Well, one whale recognised the Japanese whaling ship responsible for killing his parents. He suggested to his lady whale that they swim underneath while blowing thru their blowholes and sink it.

'The ship sank and left the crew splashing around in the ocean. The whales were pleased until the men started to swim safely to shore.

'We'll swim along and gobble them all up,' said the male.

'No way, count me out, said the female.

'Why?'

'Well, I went along with you on the blow-job.

'But there's no way I'm going to swallow the seamen!'

Desperate Doris

Stupid went to the post office on his birthday. 'I'm here to collect a parcel containing my birthday present,' he announced.

'Well, happy birthday,' the postal worker handed over the package. 'How old are you today?'

'Twenty six.'

'Well, have a great birthday.' Stupid walked outside and waited for the bus. Desperate Doris, the senior cit. arrived at the bus stop and sat next to Stupid.

'It's my birthday,' he said.

'If you let me feel your balls for a moment, I'll tell you your exact age.

'That's not possible.'

'I guarantee it is.'

'Okay, prove it.'

She unzipped his pants and felt around for a few minutes. 'Hmmm hmmm, aha aha,' she felt around some more, rolling her eyes and concentrating on the feel.

Just as the bus appeared, she pulled her hand away and said, 'You're exactly twenty six.'

'How could you know that?'

'I was behind you in line at the post office!'

***

'Guess what Santa,' Stupid said, 'every time I pass by the elderly gynaecologist's surgery, I see Desperate Doris the senior cit. coming out.'

'Hmmm,' said Santa, 'she probably likes his shaky hands!'

***

'Stupid could hardly wait to tell Santa the news. 'I heard Desperate Doris the senior cit. is giving $5 blowjobs.'

'Shit, that's a bit like walking a friggin' tight-rope.'

'Why?'

'Cause you wouldn't want to look down, that's why!'

***

'Santa, Desperate Doris says you shouldn't look down if you're bungee jumping.'

'Of course not, you've got to be careful with two things in life, bungee jumping and hookers.'

'Why!'

'Cause, if the rubbers break you're history!'

***

Desperate Doris hired a young male Uni student to help around the farm. At Xmas she said, 'I'm going to throw a party for you tonight to thank you for the great job you've done.'

'No shit, that's awesome.'

'I hope you can handle heavy drinking. There's gonna be a lot of grog consumed.'

'No sweat, I can hold my own.'

'And there's gonna be a lot of designer drugs floating around. Think you can handle that?'

'No problem, I've done a few drugs in my time.'

'And there's gonna be some really hot sex, lots and lots of red hot sex.'

'That's the best news yet say, what should I wear to this party? And how many guests will attend?'

'I don't give a shit what you wear.

'Cause it's just gonna be, you and me!'

Religious

'I happen to know Jesus was a woman,' Mrs. Claus said to Santa.

'Why on earth would you say that?'

'Well he went barefoot, couldn't afford a professional haircut, was expected to feed a crowd at a moment's notice and to make a meal out of nothing.

'And when he died he was only allowed three days rest because there was still more work to be done!'

***

'I think Jesus was Jewish,' the Xmas Fairy said, 'he went into business with his father, didn't he?'

'Yeah, but he stayed at home until he was thirty-three.

'So he had to be Italian!'

***

'Jesus was definitely Italian,' Fairy Floss agreed.

'He talked with his hands, drank a glass of red with every meal and wore a cross!'

***

Stupid the elf became a Born-Again and was on the bible-bashing circuit. He ignored the storm warning from the weather bureau and went ahead with his sermon on the banks of the river.

The storm broke and the rain fell down as people rushed to their cars and took off.

'I'll stay,' yelled Stupid, 'the lord will save me.'

A man rowed up in a rowboat. 'Jump in I'll get you out of here.'

'No, I'm right, the lord will save me.'

The emergency services speedboat arrived. 'Get in, the river's rising rapidly.'

'No, I'm right, the lord will save me.'

Within minutes the rescue chopper appeared overhead and proceeded to let down a rope.

'Leave me alone, the lord will save me.'

The chopper took off and the river rose. Stupid drowned and went to Heaven.

'Why didn't you save me?' He yelled at God.

'I tried,' God yelled back, 'I sent a rowboat, a speedboat and a chopper.

'What more do you want from me?'

***

Xmas eve dawned and the frantic Jewish grandmother called Santa from her mobile. 'Santa, I was just walking my little grandson along the beach and a big wave washed him out to sea. Please, Santa all I want for Xmas is for God to give him back.'

'Quick, yell out to God in a real loud voice and tell him what a good woman you've been and demand, I mean really demand, that he send the child back.'

The Jewish grandmother screamed at the top of her lungs, 'God, what you doing to me? I always go to Synagogue; never missed a day, I pray to you twice a day every day and I donate money every month to Jewish charities. So what the hell you take my little grandson for?

'God I demand you send him back right now!'

A voice boomed down.

'Alright, alright, here's your little darling back safe and sound.' And a big wave washed the child safely onto the sand.

The grandmother yelled again, 'For God's sake, what do you think you're doing?' The voice boomed back.

'What now Woman what now?'

'Well, he was wearing an expensive new hat!'

***

Mary Xmas reminded the school staff that sex education was scheduled for the next morning.

'Good grief,' said Father, 'the nuns couldn't possibly know anything about sex. I have no choice but to help out.'

He gathered the nuns together, explained the situation, unzipped his fly and whacked his treasured possession onto the table.

'This is a penis,' he announced to the shocked group.

The novice burst into laughter. 'No, Father that's nothing like a penis.

'A penis is long and thick and black!'

***

Santa went to confession. 'Forgive me Father for I have sinned, I made passionate love to my wife on top of the freezer. When she bent over to find the Xmas turkey I couldn't control myself, I ripped her clothes off and did unspeakable lustful things to her.

'The passion between us was unreal. We moaned and groaned and ended up doing sixty-niners on the floor. We were loud and sweaty and insatiable for almost an hour. I'm so ashamed Father, I ask for forgiveness.'

'Santa calm down, the lady you made love to is Mrs. Claus, your legal wife. You have not committed any sin and you are free to go with the full blessing of the church.'

'Thank you Father!' Santa cried. 'The church is so much more gracious than the supermarket.

'They banned us for life!'

***

'My mind is very mixed up at the moment Santa,' Ken Floss said, 'I have a wonderful wife and I'm risking my marriage by having an affair with a floozie.'

'Yeah, but that's God's fault, not yours!

'Why?'

'Because, although he gave you a brain and a penis, he only gave you enough blood to work them one at a time!'

***

The Priest and Santa were playing golf. Stupid the elf was filling in for the priest. On the wall of the confessional was a list of sins and the accompanying punishments to hand out.

The Xmas Fairy arrived. 'Forgive me Father for I have sinned. I gave Santa a blow-job last night.'

Blowjobs weren't on the list!

Stupid told the Xmas Fairy to wait a moment and he hurried out to ask the Alter Boys.

'What does Father give for a blowjob?'

'He usually gives us five dollars!'

***

'Santa, Sister confided in me today,' Mrs. Claus said, 'she would love to get pregnant but, just doesn't know how to go about it without offending the church.'

'That's easy,' said Santa.

'Just dress her up as a quire boy!'

***

During the Xmas off-season Stupid the elf drove a cab. A nun was his first passenger. 'I have to pick my friend up on the way,' she said.

'That's fine Sister. I hope you don't mind me telling you that all my life I've had a fantasy about screwing the arse off a nun.'

'And I have always had a fantasy about fucking a cab driver. Of course I could only allow this fantasy to happen if you were unmarried and attend church regularly. Also, you would have to take me from the back so you won't watch my face!'

'Agreed,' cried Stupid, 'and Sister, I'm not married and I go to church regularly.'

'Great, let's fuck.'

So Stupid climbed into the back seat.

When they recovered from all the puffing and panting, Stupid said, 'I really got you Sister, I'm married with children and I hardly ever go to church.'

'Got you too, the name's not Sister, its Cyril.

'And after we pick up my friend Cecil we're on our way to a costume party!'

***

The Xmas Fairy took Fairy Floss to the convent to see the new blinds in the nun's dining room. But the blinds hadn't arrived and the North Pole was experiencing a heat wave.

'Let's take all our clothes off and lie around,' Xmas Fairy said, 'that's what I always do when I'm hot.'

Just as they got comfortable, the doorbell rang. Fairy Floss offered to go to the door.

'Blind Man,' a voice called.

Fairy Floss opened the door and led the blind man into the dining room. 'I let him in because he's blind,' she said.

But, before the nuns could breathe a sigh of relief, the man spoke. 'I've never seen a dining room full of nice big tits and pussies before.

'Now, where do you want these blinds installed?'

***

Stupid arrived at the Pearly Gates. 'Before I allow you to enter Heaven,' Saint Peter said, 'you will need you to answer one question from the bible.

'What was the first thing Eve said to Adam in the Garden of Eden?'

Stupid had no idea. He couldn't possibly think of an answer and was beginning to get very upset.

'That's a real hard one,' he anguished.

'Right!' Cried Saint Peter.

And the gates flew open, the trumpets blew and Stupid was ushered into the Kingdom of Heaven!

***

The Xmas Fairy, Fairy Floss, Sister Slosh and Quire Boy arrived at the Pearly Gates together.

'Have you ever sinned Sister Slosh?' St. Peter asked.

'I once saw a priest's penis.'

'Well, splash your sinful eyes with the holy water and you may enter Heaven.'

'Have you ever sinned Fairy Floss?'

'I once touched the penis of a man, who was not my husband.'

'Well, go wash your sinful hands in the holy water and you too, may enter Heaven.'

Just then, the Xmas Fairy rudely pushed in front of Quire boy.

'Why did you push in?' St. Peter asked.

'Because I want to gargle the holy water before you make him sit in it!'

***

Santa's time was up and he found himself at the Gates of Hell.

'Welcome,' cried the devil. 'Let me show you to your very own mansion filled with sexy ladies just dying to fulfil your fantasies. Your wine cellar and gourmet kitchen never run dry, you're straight across the street from the casino, a golf course, the football field, the cricket pitch and a river full of fish. Welcome to Eternity!'

'I don't believe it,' Santa said, 'this is everything I've always wanted.'

'Well, I always aim to please. Of course, the Christians always spread propaganda about me but, the truth is I give people the things they've paid attention to during their lives.'

Just then, screaming and wailing; and gnashing of teeth could be heard in the distance.

Santa looked alarmed.

'Don't worry, that's just the Christians in their pit of fire and brimstone. I don't discriminate against anyone.

'I also give the Christians what they paid attention to in life!'

***

Mrs. Claus was having coffee with two nuns after Confession. 'I never have anything to confess,' Mrs. Claus complained, 'I'm sick of being good, for once in my life I'd like to have something to confess.'

'So would we,' cried the nuns, 'maybe we should commit one sin each this week, just so we can confess.'

The following week, the three met at Confession.

'I had sex with Reverend Bornagain,' the first nun confessed.

'Go drink the holy water and say "Hail Mary" three times,' said the priest, 'and you will be forgiven.'

The second nun confessed, 'I went shopping and bought a pile of sexy red crotch-less panties and I've worn them under my habit all week.'

'Go drink the holy water and say "Hail Mary" twice and you will be forgiven.'

Mrs. Claus began to cry. 'Don't be upset,' said the priest, 'what could Mrs. Claus have possibly done that would need to be forgiven?'

'I pissed in the holy water!'

***

'Santa did you see the Pope when you delivered to Heaven?' Sister Slosh asked.

'I sure did, seems he died on the same day as Bill Clinton.'

'Really.'

'Yep, and there was a mix-up at the gates and Bill was sent to heaven and the Pope was sent to Hell!

'Santa, that's terrible.'

'Sure was but, they fixed things the next day.

'Seems the Pope passed Bill on the elevators next morning and the Pope called out to Bill, 'I can't wait to meet the Virgin Mary.'

'That's nice, what did Bill say?'

'He said "Too late, you've missed out by one day!"

***

Sister Slosh was waiting for her flight to New York. She decided to fill in time by weighing herself on a Weight and Fortune machine. She put her coin in the slot and the machine issued her with a card stating, 'you weigh 55 kilos - you are a nun - you will visit New York.'

'Very impressive,' Sister Slosh said, 'but it probably tells everyone the same thing. I'll put another coin in just to see.'

The next card read, 'You weight 55 kilos - you are a nun - you will visit New York - you will disgrace yourself by farting in public.'

'That's disgusting, I never fart and I certainly wouldn't do it in public.'

Suddenly, she fell off the scale and ripped off a really loud fart. When she recovered from embarrassment, she put another coin in the slot and out came another card, 'You weigh 55 kilos - you are a nun - you will visit New York - a man will fuck you at this airport.'

'Now that's definitely wrong, I've taken a vow of celibacy.' Just then, the power went off and in the total darkness, Sister was raped. Her attacker fled and as she waited for the lights to come on, she knew she just had to find out what else was in store.

She put her last coin in the slot and out came another card.

'You weigh 55 kilos - you are a nun - you have farted, fucked around and missed your flight to New York!'

***

Santa delivered a beautiful baby boy to Joseph and Mary in the manger. As he made his exit, he banged his head against the top of the low entrance.

'Jesus Christ,' he cried.

'What a great name,' said Mary.

'And to think we were going to call him Santa, after you!'

***

Rumours of promiscuity and free sex at the North Pole, reached the ears of the Vatican. The Pope decided to visit and put a stop to such depravity.

He stood in the Town Square and addressed the crowd. 'I decree all forms of birth control forbidden, anyone using condoms or the pill is committing a deadly sin.'

'That's crap,' Santa yelled.

'Here at the North Pole if you don't play the fuckin' game, you don't make the fuckin' rules!'

***

Santa and Ken Floss arrived at the Pearly Gates at the same time.

'Jesus Santa, how did you die?' Ken asked.

'I froze to death it was horrible, my arms and legs stuck together and after my balls and dick turned to ice and fell off, I finally died. But Ken, what happened to you?'

'Well, I thought Fairy Floss was having an affair. So I came home unexpectedly and raced up to our bedroom but, no one was there. I tore down and checked out the cellar then I shot up to the second story guestroom, only to find it empty. And finally I raced down to the kitchen to find my lovely wife preparing dinner. And the next thing I know, I dropped dead from a massive heart attack.

'Shit Ken, what's wrong with you? Why didn't you look in the fuckin' freezer first?

'If you had, we'd both be alive!'

***

Mrs. Claus decided to join Santa after the Xmas Expo finished in Florida. She sent an email. 'Is it okay for me to join you Saturday?'

Santa had far too many cold beers before he bothered to reply. He typed his reply in the wrong email and accidentally sent it to the grieving widow of the recently departed, North Pole Vicar.

'Dear Wife, checked in, it's as hot as hell, expecting you to join me Saturday.

'Your loving Husband!'

***

Santa and Reverend Bornagain were playing golf. Santa played his first shot. 'Fuck, I missed,' he yelled.

'God will punish you,' the Reverend cautioned.

'Fuckin' shit shit shit, fuckin' shit shit shit, who gives a flying fuck?' Santa played his second shot and missed. 'Fuckin' shit shit shit, fuckin' shit shit shit.'

'God will certainly punish you.'

'Fuckin' shit shit shit, who cares?'

Instantly, the heavens opened and a bolt of lightning shot out of the sky and killed Reverend Bornagain.

And a voice boomed down.

'Fuckin' shit I missed, fuckin' shit shit shit!'

Farts Farts Farts

Rudolph crapped in the snow. Two blowflies decided to have a hot Xmas dinner. One let go with a really loud fart.

'Do you mind, where are your manners?' The other yelled.

'I'm trying to eat here!'

***

Rudolph had just crapped in the snow. Santa was shocked to see Stupid the elf lift up Rudolph's tail and give him a big kiss right on his arse. 'What the hell did you do that for?' Santa anguished.

'I've got chapped lips.'

'And that helps?'

'Sure does.

'It stops me licking my lips!'

***

Santa introduced Fairy Floss to his herd of reindeer. Rudolph ripped off a really loud fart and almost gassed everyone.

'I'm so embarrassed,' Santa said, as he quickly ushered Fairy Floss away, 'I can't apologise enough.'

'That's okay Santa, you should have kept quiet.

'I thought it was one of the reindeer!'

***

Rudolph had a magnificent voice. He was asked to audition for the Xmas quire. 'I would love to sing with the quire,' he said, but since my throat operation, I can only sing thru my bum.'

'That's different, we'd better hear you.'

Rudolph hopped up to the microphone and crapped on stage.

'Was that necessary?' the producer screamed.

'Yes it was.

'I have to clear my throat!'

***

Because the reindeer were pissed, Santa decided to leave them at home and use jet fuel to power the sleigh. When he arrived back from deliveries, Jack the elf suggested they try drinking jet fuel.

'I hear it's great,' he said, 'apparently its hangover free.'

They drank all night long and ended up smashed out of their minds. Santa awoke next day, to find he was hangover free and feeling great.

Santa called Jack. He too, felt great.

'Wanta get on the jet fuel again tonight?' Santa asked.

'We could, there's just one problem.'

'What?'

'Have you farted this morning?'

'No why?'

'Well don't, cause I'm now in the South Pole!'

***

Santa delivered to the nudist colony. He was invited to take his clothes off and become an honouree member for the day. A voluptuous blonde walked towards him and he immediately got an erection.

'You're new here,' she said in a husky voice, 'so I'll explain the rules. Because I've given you an erection, I must allow you to have your way with me.' She lay down on the soft grass, spread her legs and pulled Santa down.

After Santa got his rocks off, he wandered into the bar and ordered a triple scotch. Unfortunately he let rip with a really loud fart and the huge hairy bar tender immediately got an erection.

The bar tender jumped the bar. 'You're new here,' he said, 'so I'll explain the rules. Because you've given me an erection, you must allow me to have my way with you.'

He picked Santa up, threw him across a table and fucked him in the arse.

Santa was horrified. He retrieved his clothing and ran towards the sleigh.

The manager chased after him. 'Santa, you're leaving so early, please stay.'

'No way.'

'Why?'

'Sir, I'm middle aged and I'm lucky if I get one erection per day.

'But, you can bet your balls, I'll fart at least twenty times a day!'

***

Santa was checking out of the New York Hilton, when he realised he needed an instant crap. His room toilet wasn't working so he raced down the stairs to the toilet in the foyer, but all the stalls were filled.

In desperation he ran back to his room and pulled a huge plant out of a pot. He crapped in the pot, put the plant back and left.

Days later, he received an email.

'Dear Santa, all is forgiven just tell us where the fuck it is!'

Fishing

As Jesus walked along the pier, he noticed Fairyboy fishing with a piece of string. Although his only bait was seaweed tied to the end of the string, two massive fish lay in the basket. 'Did you catch this fish with your scant equipment?' Jesus asked.

'Sure did.'

'My God, that's a miracle and I don't even know what kind of fish it is.'

'I didn't know either Jesus but, Santa knew.

'He said it's a "Friggin' Fluke!"'

***

Jesus and Santa were discussing the pollution of the ocean. 'See that big metal pipe way out there, Jesus? That's raw sewerage running into the sea, killing dolphins and contaminating the fish.'

'That's terrible,' said Jesus, 'let's walk out and take a look.' Jesus strode off across the waves, with Santa trying to keep up. Soon Santa was knee deep in dirty water, then up to his shoulders and going deeper.

'Jesus, I need help or I'm going to drown.'

'Good God Santa!

'Why don't you be like me and just walk along the pipe?'

***

Fairyboy spoke to Jesus. 'My father says I can't have a bike for Xmas unless I get a haircut.'

'Well, what's wrong with that?'

'Well, Jesus you've got long hair.'

'True!

'But I walk everywhere!'

***

Santa and Jesus went fishing. 'Santa I wish you'd mind your language,' said Jesus.

'Sorry Jesus.' Santa thought quickly.

'This fish is called "Fuckin' Son of a Bitch!"

***

Jesus looked thoughtful as he surveyed the fish. 'Santa I wonder why they call fish, fish?'

'Probably 'cause the other four letter words were already taken!'

***

Jesus dozed off with his fishing rod in his hand, just as the gorgeous Xmas Fairy came along. 'Wake up Jesus, you've got a bite,' she cried.

'Would you please reel it in for me?' He asked.

As the Xmas Fairy landed the fish Jesus said. 'Thanks, now can you put fresh bait on my hook and cast it back in the water please?'

'Jesus, you're lazy Jesus, you really need a wife and a couple of sons to help you.'

'What a good idea!

'Now, where would I find a young girl who's already pregnant?'

***

Santa, Rudolph and Stupid the elf, took Jesus fishing. 'This fuckin' arthritis is killing me,' said Santa, 'I can hardly hold my fishing rod.'

'Here let me heal you,' Jesus offered. He laid his hands on Santa's arms and Santa was healed.

'Christ that's a fuckin' miracle, can you heal my sore leg?' Rudolph asked.

'No problem.' Jesus laid his hands on Rudolph's leg and he was healed.

'Stupid suffers from really bad back pain,' Santa said, 'Jesus, can you heal him too?'

'No problem.' But, before Jesus could lay his hands on Stupid's back, Stupid dived out of the boat and headed for shore.

'Jesus, Jesus,' he cried, 'have a heart.'

'I could lose my friggen disability pension!'

***

Santa and the Xmas Fairy sneaked away for a long weekend at a fishing resort. They were perfect companions. While Santa fished, the Xmas Fairy read the latest romance novel.

One morning Santa slept in, so the Xmas Fairy took the fishing boat, complete with all Santa's fishing gear out to the middle of the lake. She sat back and read to her heart's content until the nasty fishing inspector came along. 'Where's your fishing licence?' He demanded.

'I'm not fishing.'

'No, but and you have all the equipment, so I'm going to charge you.'

'Well, I'm going to have you charged with rape.'

'Rape, that's ridiculous, I'm not raping you.'

'No, but you have all the equipment!'

***

Fairy Floss's husband Ken took their son fishing with Santa. It wasn't long before Fairyboy arrived home sobbing his heart out.

'What's the matter with Mummy's Boy?' Fairy Floss asked.

'Daddy's fishing line snapped when he was reeling in the biggest fish we've ever seen and the fish got away.'

'You shouldn't cry about that, you should laugh.'

Fairyboy sobbed uncontrollably.

'I did, I did!'

***

Stupid the elf, decided to buy Santa a new fishing rod for Xmas. The salesman was blind. 'Just drop any rod on the counter and I'll tell you all about it from the sound and smell.'

Stupid dropped a rod. 'That's a top of the range fibreglass on special at the moment for $125.'

'Wow,' said Stupid, 'that's amazing.' He dropped a second rod.

'That's an Orion light action, $135.'

'Unbelievable.' Stupid let go with a horrendous fart. 'I'll take the top of the range fibreglass at $125.'

'Certainly Sir that will be a total of $145.'

'No it's $125.'

'Yes, but I've added $10 for the fish bait and another $10 for the extra loud duck caller!'

***

Rudolph and Dancer were just married and the happy couple chose a fishing honeymoon. The old man came with them on the luxury boat and the bride forced herself to be civil as he continuously farted and smoked his smelly pipe.

He sat between them as they fished and dined with them as they feasted on seafood and champagne. He stayed with them on the moonlit deck each night and put an end to love making by curling up on the end of the only bed, their wedding bed, complete with white satin sheets and rose- petals.

A week went by and Rudolph finally put ashore for more fishing bait. The gorgeous bride seized the opportunity. 'Darling, our honeymoon's almost over and we haven't had one moment alone. Please put your father in a cab and send him home.'

'My stinking father,' he screeched.

'I thought the prick was your father!'

***

Rudolph and his lovely bride cancelled their fishing honeymoon and followed the old man. He led them to the Old Folk's Home.

'Who are you? Can you remember your full name?'

'My name is McGuinness Magee.'

'You've evidently lived a very long life. Do you have a secret for a long life?'

'I do, I've smoked six packets of cigarettes every day since my thirteenth birthday and I drink two bottles of whiskey every night. I never exercise and I only eat junk food.'

'That's amazing,' said Dancer. 'I don't suppose you know how old you are?'

'Of course know.

'I'm twenty six tomorrow!'

***

Santa told Mrs. Claus he was going fishing. He and the Xmas Fairy had a sneaky weekend away. When he returned Mrs. Claus asked, 'Where's all the fish, didn't you catch any?'

'Of Course I did but, we guys decided we should give all our fish to the Old Folk's Home. By the way Dear you assured me you packed my after shave and breath-fresh.'

'And I did.

'I packed them safe and sound in your new tackle box!'

***

Santa was fishing along a lonely river when his boat capsized. He was afraid of crocodiles so instead of swimming to shore, he climbed on top of the upturned boat. Hours passed and finally a Native boy appeared on the river's bank. 'Are there crocodiles in this river?' Santa yelled.

'Santa, there haven't been any crocs around for as long as I can remember.'

'Thanks,' Santa yelled as he dived in. When he surfaced and headed for shore, he again called out to the boy. 'How did you get rid of the crocs?'

'We didn't.

'Those bloody big freshwater sharks ate them!'

***

Stupid the elf and Santa planned a fishing trip. 'I'll pack you some sausages in case you don't catch any fish,' Mrs. Claus said, 'you can cook them over the campfire the same way you cook fish.'

They returned empty handed. 'Just as well I packed sausages,' Mrs. Claus remarked smugly.

'The sausages were fuckin' useless, weren't they Stupid?'

'Sure were.

'By the time Santa and I skinned and gutted the buggers, there was nothing left!'

***

Santa and Stupid the elf took the Irish Priest out in Santa's old fishing boat. 'Bugger, I've forgotten my fuckin' rod,' Santa said as he stepped out of the boat and walked across the water to the shore.

The Priest couldn't believe his eyes or his ears.

When Santa returned, Stupid said, 'Fuck, I forgot to go have a crap before I left home.' He too, stepped out of the boat and walked across the water.

The Irish Priest decided he couldn't be outdone by these foul-mouthed, North Pole sinners, he said a silent prayer to the Virgin Mary, stepped out of the boat and sank to the depths of the lake.

'Jesus, Stupid,' Santa yelled.

'I asked you to tell Father about the bloody sandbank!'

***

Fairy Floss's credit cards were maxed out and Xmas was approaching.

'Why don't you take a stall at the markets and sell Dancer lobster tails,' the Xmas Fairy suggested, 'they're very popular at this time of year.'

So, Fairy Floss hired a stall and put up a sign **'Dancer Lobster Tails $1 each.'**

Along came Rudolph. 'Shit, that's cheap. Are they fresh? Are they small? Are you sure they're not green?'

'They're fresh, they're big and they're certainly not green,' Fairy Floss assured him.

'Okay I'll take one, here's my dollar.'

Fairy Floss led him behind her counter, sat him in a comfortable chair and began.

'Once upon a time, in a land far away, there lived a Dancer lobster…!'

***

'Santa, what's the difference between a man's favourite fishing spot and a woman's G-spot?

'I'll bite what?'

'Well, a man will spend the whole day trying to find the right fishing spot!'

***

Mrs. Claus wanted fish for dinner. Santa arrived home without any. 'Didn't you catch anything at all?' She demanded.

'Yes I did, a little sardine latched onto my line and then a big brim latched onto the sardine.'

'Well, where's the big brim?'

'A bloody big shark came along and latched onto the brim.'

'Well, shark's edible. Where the fuck's the shark? Are you telling me you didn't even manage to land the shark?'

'Well, how could I?

'The fuckin' sardine let go!'

***

Santa and the Xmas Fairy had an exhausting, lustful night of passion and debauchery. Santa fell asleep and woke in the early hours of the morning.

'My wife's waiting up for me,' he cried, 'she'll kill me.'

'Just do as I say and you'll be fine. Put your boots on, stand in a tub of water and walk back and forward thru the long grass. Then go home and tell your wife you've been making out with me all night.'

'Are you sure?'

'Positive.'

Santa followed instructions and sneaked in thru the front door.

'No use asking what you've been up to,' Mrs. Claus screamed. 'You've never told the truth in your life.'

'I've been making out with the Xmas Fairy, we're having an affair.'

'Affair my arse, I knew you couldn't tell the truth. Your legs are soaked and your boots are covered in grass. You've been fishing all night with your useless mates.

'And to make things worse, you try to blame a woman!'

***

Santa and Mrs. Claus stood on the sand and threw their lines into the surf. It was late afternoon, a favourite feeding time for sharks.

Mrs. Claus hooked a big fish and as she tried to bring it in, her line tangled in seaweed. Santa grabbed the line. 'Quick, don't stand there!

'Race in and untangled the fuckin' thing, before the sharks get it!'

***

Mrs. Claus and the Xmas Fairy were having coffee. 'Mrs. Claus, can you tell me why men always exaggerate about the size of any fish they catch?'

'Yes Dear.

'It's because they wouldn't have a clue how long six inches is!'

***

'Mrs. Claus, I wish I could cure my husband of coming home late after fishing with his mates,' Fairy Floss said.

'Well you can Dear, just do what I do and it will stop him dead in his tracks.'

'Really, what do you do?'

'Whenever I hear him coming in late I yell, "Is that you Angelo my lover?"

'How does that stop him?'

'Well, my husband's name is Santa!'

***

Santa and Rudolph fished together every week for two years, before Mrs. Claus ran off with Rudolph.

'You must feel such a sense of grief and loss,' the Xmas Fairy sympathised, 'it might help to talk about it.'

'You are such a good friend,' said Santa, 'and I do need to talk about my loss.

'I'll probably never get over losing Rudolph!'

***

'Santa, every time I'm about to go fishing my wife comes out of the kitchen and nags,' Stupid the elf complained.

'Well, maybe you should think about shortening the bitch's chain!'

***

Stupid the elf was on his first fishing trip to Texas. As he fished from the wharf, a stranger approached. 'Have you caught anything big?' He asked.

'Yes, every one of the fifty fish I caught yesterday was bigger than my wife's big fat arse, big, big, big.'

The stranger pulled a badge from his pocket. 'Well, I happen to be the fishing inspector and if you don't have a licence I'm going to see you get a big, big, big, fat fine. And I'll lock you up in a big, big, big, fat cell!'

'Shit,' said Stupid as he thought quickly for the first time in his life. 'Let me introduce myself Sir.'

He took a sweeping bow.

'I'm Little Elf the Liar, the teller of the biggest fuckin' lies in all of Texas big, big, big. He proceeded to tap dance down the wharf towards freedom.

'No one can tell lies as big as mine big, big, big!'

***

'Santa, I caught a fish without eyes,' Fairyboy said, 'what sort of fish could it be Santa? Where is it from?'

'If it hasn't got eyes, it's from New Zealand of course. It's a Fsh.

'New Zealand is the only country in the world to have Fsh!'

***

Fairy Floss's husband Ken couldn't find the address of the piano tuner in the busy shopping strip. He walked into a fish shop to ask for help.

'I'm looking for the Piano Tuner,' he said to the obliging Greek man behind the counter.

'You come to the righta place,' Spiro said.

'One pounda tuna comin' right up!'

***

Santa went to the blind man's fishing store. The blind man was covered in bruises.

'What the fuck happened to you?' Santa asked.

'I had another argument with my wife. Every time I answer her back, I end up like this.'

'What a bitch, does she belt you up?'

'No. She just changes the furniture around!'

Girls Girls Girls

Mrs. Claus and the Xmas Fairy were discussing plastic surgery. 'I'm thinking of having my boobs enlarged,' the Xmas Fairy confided.

'And I'm thinking of having my arsehole bleached,' Mrs. Claus announced.

The Xmas Fairy looked shocked.

'I don't think you could possibly bleach Santa any whiter than he is!'

***

'Can I ask what you do with your arsehole before you have sex?' The Xmas Fairy asked Mrs. Claus.

'Of course, Dear.

'I just drop him off at the toy factory!'

***

Mrs. Claus and the Xmas Fairy were discussing God. 'Well, I think God is a woman,' the Xmas Fairy said.

'Oh no, Dear. God certainly isn't a woman.

'If God were a woman, sperm would taste like chocolate!'

***

Mrs. Claus, Mrs. Sleaze and the Xmas Fairy were discussing men. 'Mrs. Claus, when you were first in love did you have a naughty nickname for Santa?' The Xmas Fairy asked.

'Well, yes Dear. I used to call him 7-Up.'

'Why?'

'Because he's seven inches long and when we were first together, it was always up. Do you have a name for your secret lover Dear?'

'Well, yes. I call him Scotch Whiskey.'

'But, isn't that a hard liquor?'

'Yes it is, Mrs. Claus.

'It is!'

***

'When Ken and I were first married,' Fairy Floss said, 'I used to call him The Miner, because of his amazing shaft.'

'Really Dear,' said Mrs. Sleaze, 'I call my husband the Postman From Hell.'

'But, why?'

'Because he never delivers on time and always puts it in the wrong box!'

***

When Fairy Floss was pregnant with Fairyboy she chose the name Agatha for a baby girl. Ken hated the name and asked Santa for help. 'How on earth can I stop her calling the baby Agatha?'

'That's easy,' said Santa.

'Just tell her you're thrilled with the name, because it reminds you of hot little Agatha you fucked in High School!'

***

'Mrs. Claus, do you know why those horrible, blonde jokes are so short,' the Xmas Fairy asked.

'Of course, Dear.

'They're short so men can remember them!'

***

'Do you remember the first time you had sex?' Mrs. Claus asked Fairy Floss.

'Oh yes and Grandmother warned me never to let a boy get on top of me, or my family would be disgraced.'

'And what happened Dear?'

'Well, to protect my family I made sure I got on top.

'Then, his family was disgraced!'

***

'Do you remember your first date, Dear?' Mrs. Claus asked Fairy Floss.

'Of course, the weather was freezing and I'd forgotten my gloves but, I remembered Grandma saying, "When your hands get cold put them between your thighs and they'll warm up."

'And what happened Dear?'

'Well, when I told my date why I kept my hands between my thighs he asked if he could put his frozen dick there to warm it up.'

'What a Son of a Bitch, I guess you learned a lot about dicks that night, Dear.'

'Yes, I did Mrs. Claus.

'I learned they really make a mess when they thaw out!'

***

'That's a very thin book you're reading Mrs. Claus,' the Xmas Fairy said.

'Of course, Dear.

'It's called, "Everything men know about women!"'

***

'Mrs. Claus, have you noticed how ugly Mrs. Sleaze's new baby is?'

'Yes Dear. When he was born the doctor slapped his mother.

'And the plastic surgeon wanted to add a tail!'

***

'Mrs. Claus, do you think Mrs. Sleaze's new baby will be alright?'

'Yes Dear. The mosquitoes won't go near him.

'And he's being breast fed by the family dog!'

***

'Did you know Mrs. Sleaze's new baby was born laughing Dear?'

'No, Mrs. Claus I did not.'

'Well, the poor little pet was laughing his little head off, with his little fingers clenched tight and tears running down his tiny cheeks.'

'Do you know why he was laughing Mrs. Claus?'

'Well, yes Dear.

'When they unclenched his fingers, he was holding a birth control pill!'

***

Fairy Floss and Ken had just returned from their honeymoon.

'Fairy Floss, let me give you the special recipe for Irish stew,' Mrs. Claus said, 'and I'll guarantee you a gourmet meal every time.'

'But Ken doesn't like Irish stew.'

'Of course not, Dear.

'And every time you mention your special recipe for Irish stew, I guarantee he'll say, "Let's eat out!"'

***

Mrs. Claus was known as the North Pole gossip. So, when Fairy Floss and Ken first became lovers, they assured her they were only flat-mates. She invited herself to dinner. 'Oh, do tell me you're sleeping together,' she gushed, 'I won't tell a soul.'

'We are not sleeping together, we're just friends.' They showed her their separate rooms.

After Mrs. Claus left, Fairy Floss couldn't find the salt and pepper shakers.

'If we don't find them by next week, I'll call her,' Ken said.

A week went by without any sign of the salt and pepper shakers. Ken called Mrs. Claus.

'Why don't you admit you're having sex?' Mrs. Claus Said.

'We're not. I just want to know what happened to our salt and pepper-shakers.'

'Got you!

'If you were sleeping in your own bed, you would have found them a week ago!'

***

When Fairy Floss and Ken first married, Fairy Floss wore only her birthday suit at home. Every time Mrs. Claus visited, she found Fairy Floss naked. 'I call it my love dress,' Fairy Floss said, 'I wear it in case Ken pops in. it's guaranteed to spice up a marriage.'

Mrs. Claus decided to try it. That night, she met Santa at the door, wearing only her bare skin. 'What the fuck, do you think you're doing?' Santa yelled.

'I'm wearing my love dress, Dear. It's guaranteed to spice up our marriage.'

'Bull shit.

'You'd have to iron the friggin thing first!'

***

Mrs. Claus met a frog when she was young and looking for a husband who could 'be walked on' and yet fully support her.

The frog hopped onto her lap and said, 'Pretty one, I was a handsome prince until a wicked witch turned me into a frog. If you will kindly kiss me, I will turn back to the handsome devil I once was. I promise to marry you and bring you to my family home, where my mother will train you in the ways of looking after me and bearing and rearing my children. She will teach you to cook my favourite foods and wash and iron my shirts the way I like best.'

Later that evening, Mrs. Claus laughed to her self as she dined on a sumptuous meal of frog legs sautéed in ginger and coconut sauce.

'I don't think so Mr. Frog, I don't fucking well think so!'

***

Mrs. Claus was helping out at the new North Pole restaurant. She was shocked to see a group of Japanese tourists jacking off at the table. 'What do you think you're doing?' She yelled.

'We berry much want to be served,' one said.

'And you think this disgusting display, will help?'

'Of course, sign say "First come, first served."

***

Ken Floss's staff consisted of his wife Fairy Floss and Jack the elf. Times were tough and one of them had to go. Jack had a large family to feed, so Ken decided to sack his own wife.

'Darling, my heart is heavy and I have a real problem,' he explained. 'I have to either lay you or jack, off.'

'Well, you'd better jack off.

'I have a blinding headache!'

***

The golf pro was giving the Xmas Fairy a lesson. 'Hold your golf club as firm as you like Santa to hold your breasts.' She followed his instructions and hit the ball 300 yards.

'Excellent, now try holding the club the way Santa likes you to hold his dick.' She did and the ball hardly moved at all.

'No good, forget Santa,' the Pro said.

'Take the club out of your mouth and hold it with your hands!'

***

Fairy Floss was pissed off because Ken wouldn't give her the money to buy a pair of expensive crocodile boots. 'I'll show you,' she fumed, 'I'll catch my own crocodiles and get my boots for nothing.'

She took his rifle and headed for the river. When Ken stopped laughing, he decided he'd better make sure she was safe.

He found her waist deep in water with a huge croc swimming her way. She took aim, shot the croc and heaved it up on the bank then piled it on top of six dead ones.

Ken couldn't believe her accuracy. 'You're an incredible shot,' he said.

'I know, but I'm going to give up now that I've shot seven.

'I can't believe that out of seven crocodiles there's not one wearing boots!'

***

When the Xmas Fairy grew old, she moved into the North Pole Nursing Home. She spent her days roaring up and down the halls in a wheel chair, making revving sounds like a car.

Santa too, had grown old. He staggered out of his door and said, 'Excuse me Ma'am I need to see your licence. You were speeding.'

The Xmas Fairy gave him a pharmacy receipt from her pocket. Santa read it, handed it back and gave her a caution.

She tore up and down the hall again and once more Santa stopped her. 'Excuse me Ma'am you're driving in a reckless manner. I need to see your car registration.'

Xmas Fairy searched her other pocket and came up with a chocolate wrapper. Santa looked it over, handed it back and gave her another warning.

Later, she tried to roar down the hall again, but a stark naked Santa blocked her way. He sported an upstanding erection.

'Oh no,' the elderly Xmas Fairy cried.

'Not the breathalyser test again!'

***

Fairyboy, Trash and Mary Xmas had grown up. Fairy Floss, Ima Sleaze and the Xmas Fairy met for coffee. 'My darling daughter Mary Xmas is doing so well with her furniture factory,' the Xmas Fairy said, 'just lately she was able to help a needy friend out with a house full of furniture.'

'Trash is doing well too,' gushed Ima Sleaze, 'he started out as a used car salesman and now has a Ferrari dealership in every state. Why, just last week a friend of his needed wheels, so Trash gave him a brand new car.'

The Xmas Fairy and Ima Sleaze turned to Fairy Floss. 'How's your useless gay son, Fairyboy?'

'Well, Ken and I are disappointed in his lack of ambition, but he must be doing something right.

Just the other day, his friends gave him a house full of furniture and a red Ferrari!'

***

When Ken Floss and Fairy Floss were first married, Ken laid down the law. 'I'll be home when I like, if I like and as late as I like. I expect a hot meal on the table the moment I arrive and I don't want any hassles.'

'No problem,' said Fairy Floss sweetly, 'just remember, they'll be red-hot sex here at exactly seven thirty every night.

'Whether you're here or not!'

***

When Ken and Fairy Floss were first married, he constantly remarked on her beautiful rear end. Fairy Floss was thrilled. She decided to surprise him and have KEN tattooed on her butt.

'Ken is a three letter word,' the Tattooist said, 'so it may look a little odd if you have two letters on one cheek and one of the other. May I suggest we use the first and last letter only? KN is almost phonetic for Ken, anyway.'

Fairy Floss agreed. She raced home and ushered Ken into the bedroom. She stripped naked and bent over and stuck her bum in the air.

Ken took one look and yelled.

'Who the fuck is KON?'

***

Fairy Floss took Santa and the Xmas Fairy for a drive in her new car. The nasty police officer pulled her over.

'Why the fuck are you only doing 25 in a 70 zone? You'll cause an accident.'

'I saw a sign saying 25.'

'That's Highway 25, the speed limit is 70.'

'Silly me, thank you Officer, I promise to read the signs carefully in future.'

Just then, Santa and the Xmas Fairy emerged from the floor. The officer noticed they were white and shaking. 'What's wrong with your passengers?'

'They'll be okay now.

'We just got off Highway 200!'

***

The Xmas Fairy was weaving all over the road. The breathalyser squad pulled her over. 'You appear to have been drinking,' an officer said, 'please blow into this.'

'Hmm,' he said as he read the result, 'looks like you've had a few good stiff ones today.'

The Xmas Fairy looked shocked.

'It can tell that, too!'

***

Santa and the Xmas Fairy were necking in the sleigh. 'Don't get too carried away,' she said, 'I'm a virgin and I intend to stay one.'

'Well, how about a blowjob?'

'No way.'

'How about a handjob?'

'What's that?'

'Well, when you were a kid, did you ever shake up a bottle of coke and spray the other kids?' The Xmas Fairy nodded.

'Well, it's the same thing.'

So Santa put his dick in her hand and the Xmas Fairy enthusiastically took hold and commenced to 'shake it up'.

A few seconds later, blood poured from Santa's nose and mouth, smoke bellowed from his ears and he screamed in pain.

'What's wrong?' The Xmas Fairy cried.

'Take your finger off the end!'

***

When Ken Floss first decided to marry, he made up his mind to choose a virgin. He attended church to meet a potential bride. After he'd taken a sweet young thing out a few times, he whipped out his cock and asked, 'Do you know what this is?'

'Of course, it's a cock.'

He gave Sweet Young Thing the big heave-ho and began seeing Fairy Floss.

On their third date, he whipped his cock out again. 'Do you know what this is?' He asked.

'Yes,' she giggled shyly, 'it's your pee-wee.' He immediately asked for her hand in marriage!

As the months went by, his new wife began to annoy Ken. She continued to refer to his dick as a pee-wee.

'This is not a pee-wee,' he finally yelled, 'this is a dick, a real dick.'

Fairy Floss doubled up with laughter.

'That's not a real dick.'

'A real dick is long and thick and black!'

***

The Xmas Fairy and Fairy Floss were flying from the North Pole to Hawaii. The pilot's voice came over the intercom. 'We have lost an engine but, no need to worry, we have three engines left. However, our flight will now take an hour longer.'

Half an hour later the pilot spoke again. 'Sorry Folks, we seem to have lost another engine but, two engines will carry us safely home. Our flight will now take two hours extra.'

'Shit,' said Fairy Floss, 'I hope we don't lose the last two engines.'

'If we do, we'll be up here all fuckin' night!'

***

Fairy Floss was on a flight to London. As she sat in her economy seat, the doorway to First Class opened, revealing a vacant seat. Fairy Floss got up and hurried into First Class, sat down and fastened the safety belt. Instantly, a diligent airline attendant appeared, 'Ma'am you must move back to Economy immediately.'

'I will not, I'm staying in First until we get to London.'

'You can't do that.'

'No, just watch me.'

The airline attendant went straight to the captain. The captain laughed. 'She sounds like a blonde.'

'She is a blonde.'

'Well, let me handle this. I'm married one and I know exactly how to handle blondes.'

Captain walked down to where Fairy Floss sat and whispered in her ear. She instantly got up and hurried back to Economy.

'What on earth did you tell her?' The airline attendant asked.

'I told her First Class wasn't going to London!'

***

Fairy Floss took Mrs. Claus cycling down a very rough street. 'I've never come this way before,' Mrs. Claus gasped thru rattling teeth.

'Really,' Fairy Floss yelled.

'It must be the cobblestones!'

***

Mrs. Claus walked into the chicken shop and asked to see a dressed chicken. The man behind the counter wore gloves. He carefully picked a chicken up with tongs and placed it on crisp, white, folded paper.

He was horrified to see Mrs. Claus lift up each wing and sniff underneath. Next, she lifted the legs and sniffed between them.

He quickly snatched the chicken away. 'Do you mind Madam?

'If you can pass the same test, I'll allow you to buy it!'

***

Mrs. Claus, the Xmas Fairy and Fairy Floss decided to find out the truth about their husbands' late nights. They hid in the loft above Santa's workroom and listened in.

Just as the girls expected, at closing time out came the booze and Rudolph could be heard making a call to invite the local hookers down.

Fairy Floss sneezed and the men froze. Santa sent Stupid up to the loft to check it out. The girls hid in some empty toy sacks.

'There's nothing here except some old toy sacks,' Stupid yelled.

'Give them a hard kick to make sure they're empty.'

He kicked the first sack and Mrs. Claus yelled 'Meow.'

'There's a cat in the first one.'

He kicked the next one. The Xmas Fairy called 'Ruff ruff.'

'There's a dog in that one.'

Stupid kicked the last one extra hard and Fairy Floss yelled.

'Xmas Toys, Xmas Toys!'

***

Earlier in life Fairy Floss decided if Ken wouldn't commit to marriage, she would throw herself in the harbour and end it all. As she sat crying on the docks a handsome sailor came along.

'Don't end it,' he begged. 'Start a new life, I'm off to Miami tomorrow and you can stow away on my ship, I'll bring you food and wine and the only thing I ask in return, is lots of sex every night.'

Fairy Floss decided she had nothing to lose. The handsome sailor hid her in a small windowless cabin below the deck, he looked after her and made love to her each night until dawn.

A week later, the captain discovered her. 'How dare you stowaway on my ship,' he yelled.

'I have an agreement with the handsome sailor. He's taking me to Miami and in return, I'm letting him screw me.'

'I'll say he's screwing you.

'You're on the North Pole ferry!'

***

'Men think all blondes are stupid,' Fairy Floss said to Mrs. Claus. 'I'm blond and if anyone were to tell me the name of any state in any country, in the whole wide world, I could actually tell them its capital!'

'Really Dear, that's amazing. Can you tell me the capital of the American state of California?'

'C!'

***

The Xmas Fairy placed an ad in the paper. 'Wanted - man who doesn't raise his fists to females - will stay forever and make love every night.'

Soon there was a loud knock at her door. She flung the door open, to find a legless and armless man. 'I don't have arms so I can't raise my fists, I don't have legs so I'll never leave you,' he cried.

'What makes you think you're capable of making love every night?'

'Well, I rang the doorbell, didn't I?'

***

Ken Floss decided to give up sex for Lent so Fairy Floss helped by locking him out of the bedroom each night.

Lent was finally over and a loud knocking woke Fairy Floss from a deep sleep.

'Knock knock, guess who?'

'I know who.'

'Guess what I want?'

'I know what you want.'

'Guess what I'm knocking with?'

***

Fairy Floss was speeding. The friendly police officer ordered her to stop and asked to see her licence. 'You police are so stupid, yesterday you took my licence away.

'And today, you expect me to show it to you!'

***

Ken Floss was worried about money. As they lay in bed, he grabbed Fairy Floss by the boobs and said, 'If we could get milk from these we could sell the cow.' He slapped her on the bum and said, 'If you could only lay eggs we could sell the hens.'

Fairy Floss was pissed off, she grabbed his dick and yelled, 'And if you could only get this up.

'We could stop feeding your brother!'

***

The Xmas Fairy and Fairy Floss collided with another car, wrecking both vehicles completely. No one was hurt.

'We are so pleased to see you're not injured,' Fairy Floss said to the male driver, 'maybe we were destined to meet.'

'You girls are charming. It's a pleasure to meet such lovely young ladies, in spite of the circumstances.'

'Oh look, our bottle of champagne is not broken,' cried the Xmas Fairy, 'maybe we should drink to our good fortune in meeting you.'

'How nice, thank you,' the man said as he pulled the top off. He drank half the bottle and then handed it back.

The Xmas Fairy held the bottle, while Fairy Floss tried to push the cork back in.

'Aren't you having any?' He asked.

'No way, we'll just wait for the police!'

***

'Mrs. Claus and Fairy Floss were discussing Women's Secret Business. 'Why do we stop bleeding when we enter the menopause?' Fairy Floss asked.

'Because we need to direct that blood to our varicose veins, Dear!'

***

'Did you know there are four kinds of sex for married woman Dear?'

'No,' said the Xmas Fairy, 'what are they?'

'House sex, when you're first married you have sex all over the house.

'Then Bedroom sex, after you've been married awhile you only have sex in the bedroom.

'Next comes Hall sex. After you've been married for years you pass each other in the hall and say, "Fuck you." And last of all, there's Courtroom sex.'

'What's courtroom sex?'

'When your lawyer fucks him in the divorce court and takes everything!'

***

'You know Dear men treat a clitoris the same way they treat anniversaries and toilets.'

'How's that Mrs. Claus?'

'Well, they always miss!'

***

'Mrs. Claus, did you know that women don't blink during foreplay?'

'Of course not, Dear.

'They don't have time!'

***

'Married woman should always act like tornadoes,' Mrs. Claus said to the Xmas Fairy.

'How's that.'

'Moan like hell when they come and take the house when they leave!'

***

'Mrs. Claus, can I ask how you first knew when Santa was finally planning for the future?'

'Of course, Dear.

'It was when he bought two cases of scotch, instead of one!'

***

'Mrs. Claus, how did you know when your honeymoon was over?'

'When he no longer laughed at burnt toast, Dear!'

***

'I don't know whether to get a dog or a husband,' the Xmas Fairy confided to Mrs. Claus.

'Get a dog, Dear.

'After a year, the dog will still be pleased to see you!'

***

'Mrs. Claus, the new man in town sent flowers. Do you think I should put my legs in the air for him?'

'Of course not, Dear.

'Just buy a vase!'

***

'Once you marry them, men expect women to be like the local convenience store.'

'What do you mean?'

'Open twenty four hours a day, Dear!'

***

'I have to shop for new lingerie and good panties are so expensive. I wonder why I bother to wear them?' The Xmas Fairy said

'They probably keep your ankles warm, Dear!'

***

'I'd like to buy a wonder-bra, Mrs. Claus. I wonder why they call them wonder-bras?'

'That's easy, Dear.

'When girls take them off, they wonder where their breasts went!'

***

'Mrs. Claus, I heard the North Pole Witch always take her panties off before she rides her broomstick.'

'That makes perfect sense, Dear.

'Probably gives her better traction!'

***

'Mrs. Claus, the North Pole Witch says that all female sky-divers wear jockey straps.'

'That makes sense, Dear.

'Probably stops them whistling on the way down!'

***

'Mrs. Claus, I heard that the North Pole Witch has a pierced belly button.'

'Hmm, I suppose it's a handy place to hang her air freshener Dear!'

***

'Mrs. Claus, why do men find it so difficult to make eye contact?'

'Because breasts don't have eyes, Dear!'

***

'Mrs. Claus, I don't know whether to go to the singles bar or the circus?

'Depends if you prefer talking or non-talking clowns, Dear.'

'Whatever do you mean Mrs. Claus?'

'Well, at the circus the clowns don't talk.'

***

'I hope you don't mind me saying so Mrs. Claus, but Santa is so macho.'

'You're so right, Dear.

'Would you believe, he jogged home from his own vasectomy?'

***

'I worry about that big bull Santa bought Mrs. Claus. How does the poor thing keep warm in all the snow?'

'He's male, Dear.

'He probably just wanders into the barn and slips into a nice warm jersey!'

***

'I just love your snowman Mrs. Claus. I don't suppose there's any difference between a male snowman and a female one?'

'Not much Dear.

'Just snowballs!'

***

'I just love the snow bunnies, Mrs. Claus. I bet they have soft sex.'

'Why's that Dear?'

'They've probably got cotton balls!'

***

'Mrs. Claus, I heard Fairy Floss's husband Ken, dyed his blonde hair black. What do you think of that?'

'Artificial intelligence, Dear!'

***

'Mrs. Claus, I'm a little worried about Fairy Floss. She's not having any luck with pregnancy and she's always got a bruised belly button.'

'Of course, Dear!

'She's got a blonde husband!'

***

'Fairy Floss reminds me of men and beer bottles if you don't mind me saying so, Dear?'

'What on earth do you mean, Mrs. Claus?'

'You know, empty from the neck up!'

***

'Mrs. Claus, did you know Fairy Floss was so short of money she couldn't afford to fill her car up?'

'I know, Dear.

'She sold her car to pay for the fuel!'

***

'I always take Fairy Floss with me when I go Xmas shopping,' Mrs. Claus remarked to the Xmas Fairy.

'That's nice Mrs. Claus, but why?'

'I get to park in the handicapped zone!'

***

'Where on earth, are the computer games from Japan?' Santa asked the elves. 'Why are they late?'

'Well, we used the Xmas Fairy's girls only, delivery Service called "Feel Like It," a terrible mistake.'

'Why?'

'Well, they only deliver when they fucking well feel like it!'

***

'Stupid, you'd better call the Xmas Fairy at "Feel Like It" and complain about the late deliveries.'

'No way Santa, there's only a slight difference between her girls-only staff and wild dogs.'

'Yeah what's that?'

'Lipstick!'

***

'Santa I did call "Feel Like It" and ask when we can expect our deliveries.'

'I hope they said "ASAP."'

'No! They said "FWFLI."'

'What the hell's "FWFLI?"'

'When they fuckin' well feel like it!'

***

On their honeymoon night, Ken Floss asked Fairy Floss to pose naked for a photo of her loveliness. She retrieved her camera and asked him to pose naked too.

'Oh my goodness,' she gasped.

Ken was thrilled. 'Do you want a picture of my penis for your wallet, my angel?'

'No.

'I want a picture of your penis, so I can get it enlarged!'

***

Fairy Floss and Ken Floss were just married. 'Please be gentle, I'm a virgin,' she said.

'How come, haven't you been married three times?'

'Yes and my first husband was a gynaecologist and all he wanted to do was look at it. My second husband was a psychologist and all he wanted to do was talk about it.

'My darling third husband was a stamp collector!'

'And?'

'Oh, how I miss that man!'

***

Fairy Floss and Ken Floss were walking thru the park when they were overcome with passion. After about ten minutes, Ken came up for air. 'I wish I had a torch,' he said.

'So do I,' sighed Fairy Floss.

'You've been eating ivy for ten minutes!'

***

Santa was pulled over for speeding. 'You were flying way above the speed limit,' the officer said.

'I bloody well wasn't.'

'Yes, you were.'

'I fucken well was not.'

'And you're using bad language.'

'I am not, you prick.'

'Don't waste your time, Officer,' Mrs. Claus remarked.

'When Santa's pissed there's no use arguing with him!'

***

Santa was pissed off with deliveries. Mrs. Claus was filling in. The Highway Patrolman pulled along side the sleigh as it sped along the freeway. He was shocked to see her knitting as she drove.

'Pull over,' he yelled.

Mrs. Claus yelled back.

'No no Officer, its socks for Santa!'

***

'When's your birthday?' Rudolph asked Fairy Floss.

'December.'

'What day?'

'The sixth.'

'What year?'

'Every year, Dummy!'

***

Fairy Floss borrowed Santa's sleigh to take the Elves to Wonderland. They were almost there when she noticed a large sign reading: **'Wonderland Left.'**

So she turned the sleigh around, said 'Bugger.'

And took the Elves back home!

***

Santa was having a break. The Xmas Fairy and her cousin Fairy Floss were in charge of the sleigh. They parked in the shopping centre car park and accidentally locked the keys in.

After borrowing a coat hanger from the dress shop and trying unsuccessfully to open the sleigh door, there was a flash of lightning and the sky darkened over.

'Hurry up, do something,' Fairy Floss screamed.

'It's beginning to rain and the top's down!'

***

Santa's Mother was Jewish. When Santa first brought the young Mrs. Claus home, his mother asked, 'What's her name?'

'Goldberg Mumma.'

'Thank Goodness, what's her first name?'
'Whoopi Mumma!'

***

Santa moved out of home. He left a note for Mrs. Claus. 'I turned fifty four today and have moved into the North Pole Motel with a sexy eighteen year old.'

When he arrived at the motel, a message from Mrs. Claus was waiting. 'I too, am fifty four and by the time you receive this, my eighteen year old toy boy will have moved into home.

'And let me tell you that eighteen goes into fifty four more times, than fifty four goes into eighteen!'

***

The Xmas Fairy and Cousin Fairy Floss were driving thru the small town of Tumbi Umbi in Australia's state of New South Wales. They were arguing over the correct pronunciation of the town's name.

After stopping for a coffee and burger, Fairy Floss asked the blonde cashier if she would settle their argument.

'Would you please tell us very slowly and clearly, exactly where the fuck we are.'

The cashier lent forward and answered slowly and clearly.

'You're at fucken Burger King!'

***

'I dread to think of my fortieth birthday,' Mrs. Claus said to the Xmas Fairy.

'How awful, did something terrible happen?'

***

'Santa, I know we give toys to the children at Xmas,' Mrs. Claus said, 'but wouldn't it be wonderful if we could also find a way to help the hungry and homeless.'

'There is a way Dear.'

'How?'

'Just get the hungry to eat the homeless!'

***

Mrs. Claus and the Xmas Fairy attended a bridal shower for Mrs. Sleaze's niece.

'Mrs. Claus, how do you identify the bride at a Sleaze family wedding?' The Xmas Fairy asked.

'That's easy, Dear.

'Just look for the girl with new thongs!'

***

Ken Floss gave Fairy Floss an exotic, diamond-framed, hand mirror for Xmas. The Xmas Fairy admired her own reflection in Fairy Floss's mirror.

'I look really great in this mirror, surrounded by diamonds,' she announced.

'Don't be silly,' Fairy Floss said as she snatched the mirror back and held it up to her face. 'That's not you in the mirror.

'It's me in the mirror!'

Irish

Santa was drunk as a skunk. A jar of peanuts on the bar suddenly spoke. 'I like your red shirt Santa, it's very colourful.'

'Shit, I'm hearing things, I must need a smoke.' Santa staggered to the cigarette machine. The machine yelled at him.

'Get out of here, you red prick.'

Santa staggered back to the bar and explained the whole scenario to the Irish barman. 'Take no notice,' he said.

'Irish peanuts are always complimentary but, the Irish cigarette machine is often out of order!'

***

The Irish Xmas Fairy was stopped for speeding and taken to the police station. As the policeman sat down, she noticed his fly was undone.

'Oh no,' she cried.

'Not another breathalyser test!'

***

The Irish Cinders wanted to go to the ball, but she didn't have any tampons. She asked the Irish Xmas Fairy for help.

'I can wave my wand over a pumpkin from your garden and turn it into a tampon. But, you must be home by midnight or your tampon will revert back to a pumpkin.'

Cinders agreed and went to the ball. The Irish Xmas Fairy waited up but, it was dawn before Cinders finally waltzed thru the door.

'Where the hell have you been?' The Irish Xmas Fairy screamed. 'I told you to be home by midnight.'

'And I would have been if I hadn't met the sexiest man with the sexiest name.'

'What do you mean the sexiest name?'

'Peter Peter the Pumpkin Eater!'

***

The Irish Xmas Fairy found a strange little man at the bottom of her garden. She ran after him calling, 'You're an Irish leprechaun, if I catch you, you have to grant me three wishes.' The little man took off, but the Irish Xmas Fairy was too fast. She tackled him to the ground.

'Okay, I'll grant you three wishes.'

'I wish to live in a big mansion. I wish to own a fleet of prestige cars and I wish for a bank account that never empties.'

'Wow, you're really greedy. In order for me to grant these extra large wishes, you need to be my sex slave for one entire night.'

'No problem, let's make it tonight.'

The next morning the little man shook the exhausted, Irish Xmas Fairy awake. 'I just want to know how old you are,' he said.

'I'm twenty three.'

'Twenty three years old,' the little man shook his head.

'And you still believe in leprechauns!'

***

Santa returned from his rounds. He told the Xmas Fairy he was upset by the sight of two Irish statues gazing lustfully at each other across a Dublin park.

'Can you wave your wand to allow them to get their rocks off for Xmas?' He asked.

'Yes, I have the power to grant them an hour of life. I'll leave now so they can have a merry Xmas.'

The Xmas Fairy waved her magic wand over the statues and they screamed with glee and ran into the bushes. For half an hour she sat and watched the branches shake and listened to cries of 'Almost there!' and 'oh, that was amazing!'

Finally, the statues emerged hand in hand from the bushes. 'You've only used up half your time,' the Xmas Fairy said.

'Well let's do it all again,' said the female statue.

'Only this time you hold the pigeon down and I'll crap on its head!'

***

Emerald the Irish elf was getting nowhere with the female students. He didn't interest them romantically but, there was one girl who liked to talk to him.

For days he listened to her incessant chatter about getting the courage to ask her parents to send more money.

When Emerald tried to get her in the sack, she turned nasty and sent him a photo of herself sucking a fellow student's dick.

Anxious to get back in her good books, the Irish elf decided to let her parents know she was short of money.

He was out of notepaper, so he used the back of her photo to write on. 'Your daughter's short of money and doesn't like to ask.

'Please send her more money!'

***

Emerald, the Irish elf was sitting on the floor with the kids, helping to assemble the Xmas tree. His wife was sitting on the couch with her legs wide apart. As Emerald looked up, he realised she wasn't wearing panties.

'Good grief Woman. Put your legs together.

'If you're not careful, the K I D S will see your cunt.'

***

Emerald the Irish elf noticed the voluptuous girl with a mass of hair and heavy make-up, standing behind the counter in the clock shop. She wore a low-neck top, short skirt and high strappy sandals. A sign in the window read, 'Let us supply you with hands and face.'

Emerald walked in, unzipped his pants and slapped his dick on the counter.

'How dare you, what the hell do you want?'

'I want what the sign says.

'I want you to supply the hands and face to go around my dick!'

***

Stupid first met Emerald the Irish elf at the gym. Emerald had a well-muscled body and a head the size of a tennis ball.

'Do you mind if I ask how come you have such a small head?' Stupid asked.

'Not at all, it all happened when I met the Irish Genie and she granted me three wishes. I wished for the body of a champion weight lifter and my own mansion at the North Pole. She gave me both.'

'And what about your third wish?'

'I think it was my question.'

'What was your question?'

'How about a little head?'

***

The Irish surf life saver wasn't having any luck, so he decided to make a fresh start at the North Pole. He heard Santa calling for help. 'Someone's drowning and I think it's the Xmas Fairy,' Santa yelled, 'save her and I'll give you $100.'

The lifesaver dived in and brought the distraught female safely back to shore.

'Shit,' cried Santa, 'that's not the Xmas Fairy it's my bitch of a mother in law.'

'Just my rotten luck,' the Irish lifesaver said as he reached for his money belt.

'How much would I be owing you?'

***

Emerald, the Irish elf walked into the bar. 'Quick, give me a double Irish whiskey.'

'What's wrong?' asked the barmaid.

'I've just found out my eldest son is gay.'

'Well drink your drink and I'll pour you another.'

The next night Emerald returned to the bar. 'Quick, give me two doubles of Irish whiskey.'

'Why, what's wrong?'

'I've just found out my youngest son is gay.'

'Unbelievable. Well, drink up and I'll be ready with another.'

The following night he was back again. 'Quick, bring me a bottle of Irish whiskey and I'll drink it straight from the bottle.'

'Oh no, isn't anyone in your family getting any pussy?'

'Well, yes.

'I've just found out my wife is!'

***

Ken Floss had a few drinks at the Irish bar. He was astounded to see all the pretty girls hovering around the ugliest man he had ever seen.

'What's his secret?' Ken asked the Irish barman, 'I'm the most handsome man in the North Pole, but the girls head straight to him!'

'Dammed if I know,' the Irish barman puzzled, 'he just comes in here every night and orders a drink.

'Then sits there licking his eyebrows!'

***

Santa was drinking with Emerald the Irish elf at Emerald's favourite bar. 'Emerald, see that man at the end of the bar, he looks so much like you, he could be a clone.'

'Holy shit, he certainly does look like me, let's go over and talk to him.

'Excuse me Sir, but you look exactly like me, where on earth are you from?'

'Good grief, it's like looking in the mirror. I was born In Ireland at County Cork and I moved to the North Pole two years ago.'

'I can't believe my ears. I too, was born at County Cork and moved here two years ago. My name is Emerald, Emerald O'Reilly.'

'And my name is Green, Green O'Reilly.'

'Holy shit.'

So they all got stuck into the Guinness.

The barmen changed shifts. 'Anything new today?' the relieving barman asked.

'Not really.

'The O'Reilly twins are pissed out of their minds as usual!'

***

Emerald, the Irish elf was married. Green his twin was single.

Emerald's wife went to God the same day Green's old boat sank to the bottom of the lake.

Mrs. Claus met Green, coming out of the toy factory and mistook him for Emerald. 'I'm so sorry to hear of your tragic loss,' she said.

'Oh, don't you be sorry for me now,' he said. 'I can't wait to collect the insurance on that dilapidated old thing. She had a hole in her bottom and no matter how much I scrubbed her, she smelled like dead fish. To be quite honest, I was glad to see her go.'

'That's the most tragic story I've ever heard,' Mrs. Claus couldn't hold back the tears. 'How did the poor thing go?'

'Thru my own carelessness, I gave the reindeer and elves permission to use her all at once.

'And with so many climbing aboard, she just cracked right up the middle!'

Kids

Mrs. Claus was helping out at Kindy.

Fairy Floss's son sidled up. 'Please Miss Helper, do farts have lumps?'

'You shouldn't use rude words like farts Fairyboy but, no they don't have lumps.'

'Then I must have shit in my pants!'

***

The North Pole paedophile Peddy was released from jail. As he walked passed the Pre-school Mrs. Claus yelled, 'Call the police, call the police!'

'Why?' The Principal asked.

'I just heard him say he "feels like a kid again!"

***

Peddy the paedophile and his friend Phile found a pair of lost panties. Peddy placed them under his nose and sniffed, 'hmm, a six year old girl.'

Phile grabbed the panties sniffed for a moment and said, 'no, a seven year old girl.'

'Six year old.'

'Seven year old.'

'Six!'

'Seven!'

Just then the local priest came along. 'Father, do these panties belong to a six or a seven year old girl?'

Father had an extra good sniff. 'You're both wrong,' he said, 'definitely an eight year old.

'But not from my parish!'

***

Fairy Floss and Ken Floss took their son Fairyboy to a nude beach. As Fairyboy played at the water's edge, he was amazed at the different sizes and shapes of bodies. 'Mummy, there are ladies with much bigger boobies than yours,' he said.

'Just remember Son, the bigger the boobs, the dumber the lady,' Fairy Floss told him.

About half an hour later Fairyboy said, 'Mummy, there are men with much bigger dongers, than Daddy's.'

'Well, just remember Son, the bigger the donger, the dumber the man.'

Fairyboy ran down the sand to find his father talking to a nude sunbather. He raced back to his mother.

'Mummy come see, Daddy's talking to the dumbest lady I ever saw.

'And the more he talks, the dumber he gets!'

***

'Guess what happened while you were out Mummy.'

'What happened, Fairyboy Darling?'

'Well, I was playing in your closet and Daddy came upstairs with the Xmas Fairy. And they took their clothes off and got on the bed; and Daddy got on top of her and.......'

'Enough,' Fairy Floss yelled, 'wait until Daddy comes home and you can tell me all about it, while Daddy listens to every word.'

Ken arrived home to find Fairy Floss waiting beside her packed bag.

'Fairyboy, tell your father what you saw today.'

'When I was playing in the closet Daddy, I saw you and the Xmas Fairy come into the bedroom and take all your clothes off. And I saw you get on top of her.

'And then I saw you do the same thing to the Xmas Fairy that Santa does to Mummy, when you're not here!

***

Fairy Floss was shocked to see Fairyboy kick a chicken and then the cow, as he came in for breakfast. When he sat down to scrambled eggs and a big glass of milk, Fairy Floss took his breakfast away. 'You kicked a chicken so, no eggs for you. You kicked the cow so, no milk for you. I hope you get the message.'

Fairyboy sat and sulked. His father walked in, tripped and accidentally kicked the cat.

Fairyboy jumped up and clapped his hands at his mother.

'Do you want to tell him Mummy?

'Or shall I?'

***

Fairyboy and his classmate Trash were standing at the school toilets having a pee. 'Your dick doesn't have any skin on the end,' Trash announced.

'Cause not, I'm circumcised, they cut the skin off when I was a baby.'

'Yuk, I bet that hurt.'

'Sure did.

'I didn't walk for a whole year!'

***

Fairyboy showed Santa his report card, 'I only got half a question wrong in maths and they failed me,' he said.

'What the fuck was the question?'

'What's four times six. I said twenty four.'

'That's right,' said Santa, 'what was the other half of the question?'

'What's six times four.'

'What's the fuckin' difference?'

'That was my answer!'

***

Fairyboy's class received sex education for a full term from a sweet young teacher. At the end of term she had no choice but to fail both Fairyboy and Trash.

'We should get her for failing us,' Trash said to Fairyboy.

'What do we do?'

'Kick her in the balls of course!'

***

Fairyboy returned from a school excursion to a farm. 'We saw sheep, chickens, horses, bulls and fuckers,' he told his shocked father.

'You must mean cows or some other animal, not fuckers. Who said they were fuckers?'

'Well, Teacher called them heifers.

'But we all knew what she meant!'

***

Santa was alarmed to hear Fairyboy crying his heart out. 'What's wrong?'

'My Battery Bunny is dead, he's gone to God.'

'Don't be silly, your Battery Bunny's not dead. He probably needs a new battery.'

'No Santa, he died from too much sex.'

'How?'

'Well, you know how Battery Bunnies just keep going and going?'

'Yeah.'

'Well, Trash put his batteries in backwards and he just kept coming and coming!'

***

'What do you want for Xmas?' Santa asked sweet little Mary Xmas.

'I want a Divorced Barbie, please Santa.'

'What's the hell's a Divorced Barbie?'

'She comes with Ken's house and car.

'And all the rest of his stuff!'

***

It was Show or Tell time at school. 'Teacher, I haven't got any thing to show,' Fairyboy said sadly, 'but I want to tell how a period has changed my life forever.'

'How could a period change your life?'

'Well, last night when we had Santa over for dinner, my sister said she'd missed a period. And before we got to dessert, Mummy had a stroke and Daddy had a heart attack.

'Then Santa shot himself!'

***

Fairyboy was visiting with Santa. They watched a little earthworm trying to get back into a hole. 'Santa, I bet you I can put that wiggly limp worm back in the hole.'

'And I bet you five dollars, you can't.'

Fairyboy ran in doors and grabbed Mrs. Claus's hair spray. He raced back and sprayed the worm as stiff as a board, then gently eased the stiff worm back into the hole.

Santa quickly handed over five dollars, grabbed the can of hair spray and raced indoors.

Twenty minutes later, he was back with another five-dollar bill. 'But Santa, you gave me five dollars already.'

'I know.

'But this one's from Mrs. Claus!'

***

'Santa, why do men call girls birds?' Fairyboy asked.

'Hmm let me think.

'Probably 'cause they're good at picking up dirty, crawling worms!'

***

Fairyboy walked over to his grandparent's house. Grandpa was sitting on the porch naked from the waist down.

'Grandpa, don't you remember you ended up with a stiff neck, last time you sat out here in the cold with your shirt off? Maybe I'd better tell Grandma to bring you some pants.'

'Don't bother Fairyboy.

'It was Grandma's idea that I sit here with my pants off!'

***

'Where did I come from?' Fairyboy asked his mother.

'The stork brought you.'

'And where did you come from?'

'The stork brought me too. And he brought Grandma.'

'Gees, we're probably the only family in the North Pole to have three generations of abnormal births!'

***

'Where did I come from?' Trash asked his father.

'God made you.'

'And where did you come from?'

God made me and he made Grandma too.'

Not satisfied with the answers, Trash asked his mother.

'Mom, where did I come from?'

'You evolved from an ape. I evolved from an ape and so did Grandpa.'

Trash went back to his father. 'Dad, I'm confused, you say God made us and Mother says we evolved from apes!'

'Son, I was talking about my side of the family and your mother was talking about hers!'

***

Fairyboy went to the pharmacy with his father. 'What are these things Dad? They come in packs of 1, 3 and 12.'

'They're condoms. The single packs are for the high school boys, one for Friday night. The packs of three would be for the kids at Uni or college, one each for Friday Saturday and Sunday nights.'

'But what about the packs of 12, there's not twelve nights in a week!'

'They're for the married men, Son,' Ken Floss said sadly.

'One for each month of the year!'

***

Fairyboy noticed the elves using the word Pussy a lot. They also favoured the word Bitches. 'Mum, what's a pussy?' He asked.

Fairy Floss opened up the dictionary and showed him a picture of a beautiful black cat. 'That's a pussy.'

'Mum, what's a bitch?'

Fairy Floss again opened the dictionary and showed him a picture of a female sheep dog. 'That's a bitch.'

Ken Floss arrived home. 'Dad, what's a pussy?'

Ken took Men Only Magazine from under his arm, opened up the centrefold and drew a ring around the heart shaped bush of the lovely young thing. 'See this circle, everything inside the circle is a pussy.'

'Dad, what's a bitch?'

'Son, everything out side the circle is a bitch!'

***

Ken was engrossed in his favourite TV show. 'Daddy, what does a pussy look like?' Fairyboy asked.

'Before or after sex?' Ken said without thinking.

'Hmmm, before.'

'Like a beautiful pink rose with soft petals.'

'And after sex?'

'Like Santa's dog Wonder when he's been slurping milk!'

***

Fairyboy had a speech impediment. It was his first day at school. When the door of the school bus opened, Fairyboy slurred his words. 'Good morning Mr. Bus Driver.'

Before Fairyboy could board the bus, the driver slammed the door shut and took off. The next day, the same thing happened

Ken Floss was outraged. 'I'll show him,' he said, 'I'll go with you tomorrow and make sure he let's you on the bus.'

The bus arrived, the door opened and Ken let fly. 'How dare you drive off and leave my son without transport, you prick. It's bad enough the poor kid's got a speech impediment, without you treating him like shit.'

'Oh shit, I'm sorry,' the driver slurred.

'I thought he was making fun of me!'

***

'Santa, why does my dog lick his bum when he sees me coming home from school?' Fairyboy asked.

'Cause he knows he'll be licking your face in a few minutes!'

***

Santa was helping Fairyboy with his homework. 'I have to explain the difference between monogamy and bigamy,' Fairyboy said.

'There is no difference,' said Santa.

'There must be.'

'Not really, a bigamist has one wife too many.

'And a monogamist has one wife too many!'

***

'Santa, my homework gets harder every week,' Fairyboy complained, 'I have to explain the difference between ignorance and apathy.'

'No use asking me,' said Santa.

'Why?'

'Cause I don't know and I don't care!'

***

Fairyboy was staying with the Claus family while his parents were away. When Santa came home from the toy factory, Fairyboy ran to meet him. 'We've been robbed, Santa. Asians have robbed your house!'

'How do you know they were Asian? Did you see them?'

'No.

'But, my homework's done with all the right answers and your dog's missing!'

***

The residents of the Old Folks Home helped Mrs. Claus sort the Xmas mail. One letter from a child asked for $100 for Xmas. 'I need the money for a bike to deliver papers and earn money to help my poor family out.'

The old folks were touched and as it was a few months before Xmas, they passed the hat around at the Old Folks Home and collected $90. They put the $90 in a Xmas card and sent it to the deserving boy.

The boy wrote back. 'Dear Santa, thank you for the money for my bike. But next time, please don't let the Old Folks handle it.

'Those thieving, rotten, old mongrels took 10% commission out of my money.'

***

'Stupid why doesn't Santa have any little boys and girls of his own?' Fairyboy asked Stupid the elf.

'I'm not sure.

'But I did hear, he only comes once a year!'

***

Fairyboy and Trash Sleaze snuck into the strip club and watched the naked ladies strut their stuff. Fairyboy suddenly raced out the door and headed for home.

Trash caught up with him. 'What's wrong, did the naked ladies frighten you?'

'My Daddy said that boys who look at naked ladies will be turned into stone.'

'But, we haven't been turned into stone.'

'Well, something's turning hard in my pants!'

***

For years, Santa made a habit of giving a small toy to every child at the local school. This year however, he needed to cut costs. 'We'll still visit,' he explained to the reindeer, the elves and the Xmas Fairy, 'we just won't go to the unnecessary expense of giving out toys.'

When the visit was over Santa breathed a sigh of relief. 'Well, that went well and I'm pleased to see there are just as many children waving good bye today, as last year.'

'True,' said the Xmas Fairy.

'But they're holding up a lot less fingers!'

Medical

'Mrs. Xmas Fairy, I have wonderful news for you this Xmas.'

'Actually Doctor its Miss Xmas Fairy.'

'Then I have some devastating news for you this Xmas!'

***

'Mrs. Xmas Fairy, I have wonderful news for you and your husband this Xmas.'

'Doctor, I don't have a husband.'

'Then, I have some wonderful news for you and your boyfriend.'

'I don't have a boyfriend Doctor. I've never been with a man.'

Doctor rushed to open the window and look up into the sky. 'What are you doing Doctor?'

'I'm looking towards the heavens.

'The last time this happened, there was a bloody big star in the sky!'

***

Mrs. Claus asked her plastic surgeon to reduce the size of her extra large vagina lips. When she came out of the operation she was furious to find three roses on her bedside table. 'Doctor, my operation was supposed to be confidential.'

'And it is. I haven't told a soul. I always give my patients a yellow rose to let them know I care. The pink one is from the anaesthetist for the same reason.'

'But Doctor, there's a red rose. Who is it who knows and adores me?'

'The young man in the Burns Unit.

'The red rose is to thank you for his new penis!'

***

Mrs. Claus took a job at the sperm bank. On her very first day a masked gunman held her up. He forced her to open the sperm vault and drink one sample. 'Now, drink another,' he demanded.

'I can't.'

'Do it.'

'Drink two more.'

'I can't.'

'Do it.'

Mrs. Claus sucked it all down. The man took his mask off.

'See Honey, was that so friggin' hard?'

***

Santa walked into the pharmacy. 'I'd like ninety nine condoms, please.'

The gorgeous pharmacist was stunned. 'Ninety nine condoms, well, I'll be fucked.'

'No problem,' said Santa.

'Just make that, one hundred condoms!'

***

The Xmas Fairy and Fairy Floss were trying to give up smoking. 'It's so hard,' Xmas Fairy said. 'The only relief I get from cravings, is when I've popped a life saver in my mouth and sucked, sucked sucked.'

'It might work for you,' said Fairy Floss.

'But, I don't happen to live near the beach!'

***

Mrs. Claus and Fairy Floss were smoking as they waited at the bus stop. When it began to rain, Mrs. Claus took a condom from her pocket, snipped the top off and pulled it over her cigarette.

'What's that?' Fairy Floss asked.

'A condom.'

'Where did you get it?'

'From the pharmacy.'

Later, Fairy Floss went to the pharmacy, 'I'd like a condom please.'

'Certainly Ma'am, what size?'

'I'm not sure.

'I need one to fit a camel!'

***

Mrs. Claus was the new president of the hospital's fundraising committee. The committee was having a grand tour of the new wing. They entered one ward to find all the patients masturbating. 'How disgusting,' she screamed.

'Oh no Mrs. Claus, these men have testifill, a tragic condition that causes their testicles rapidly fill up with semen. They must release the semen at regular intervals or the testicles will explode and cause instant death.'

'Oh the poor things, my committee and I will raise funds for research.'

They moved on to the next ward, to find a row of gorgeous young hookers giving each patient a blowjob.

'What's the reason for this?' Mrs. Claus demanded.

'Testifull, the same tragic condition,' Doctor assured her.

'But, top of the range Private Health Cover!'

***

Jack the elf stuttered all the time. He begged Doctor to find a cure.

After a thorough examination, Doctor said, 'I've got good news and I've got bad news.'

'What's the good news?'

'I've found the cause. Because your penis is a foot long, it pulls on your lungs and the lungs pull on your voice box. This of course, causes you to stutter.'

'What's the bad news?'

'We would need to take six inches off your penis to avoid the pulling action.'

'Shit.'

'It's not as bad as you think. You would still end up with a well-endowed six inches.'

Jack had the operation. A month went by and he went back. 'Doc, it seems six-inch dicks are quite common. When I had twelve inches, I had to fight the girls off. I want my six inches back.'

Doctor looked shocked.

'Didn't you hear me Doc? I want my six inches back.'

'Nnnno wwwway, nnnno wwway!'

***

Santa rushed to a specialist the morning after he failed to get an erection. The specialist advised him to have an operation immediately. 'The muscles at the base of your penis are worn out and need to be replaced with muscles from the base of a baby elephant's trunk.'

Six weeks after the operation, Santa was told to try sex again. He took the Xmas Fairy to dinner, to celebrate.

Half way thru dinner, he felt an incredible pressure in his pants.

'Unzip your pants,' the Xmas Fairy said, 'no one will notice.'

Suddenly, Santa's dick crept out and felt its way up to the table. It sniffed around for a few seconds and then grabbed a bread roll and shot back into his pants.

'Santa, that was amazing, can you do it again?'

Santa looked at her thru painful crossed eyes.

'Shit no.

'There's no way I can fit another bread roll up my arse!'

***

Santa crashed the sleigh, he woke up in hospital. 'Doctor, what's wrong with me, I can't feel my fuckin' legs.'

'Of course not.

'We had to amputate your fuckin' arms.'

***

'What's wrong with Mrs. Claus?' Santa asked her Doctor.

'I won't know until Monday when her test results come back. But, it's either Alzheimer's or Aids!'

'Shit Doc, that's terrible. What can I do in the meantime?'

'Well, you could take her to the park and leave her, then go home and wait to see if she finds her way back. But, if she does find her way home please head my warning.

'Do not under any circumstances, fuck her!'

***

'Do you have two dogs Mrs. Claus?' The pharmacist asked.

'No I only have Wonder, why?'

'Well, you buy two packets of dog vitamins each week.'

'That's because Santa takes one packet himself, he says they're so much stronger than human vitamins.'

'That's dangerous, taking animal products can cause death in a human.'

It was two weeks before Mrs. Claus came in again. 'How's your husband?' The pharmacist asked.

'He died last week.'

'I'm so sorry Mrs. Claus but, I warned you those vitamins were dangerous.'

'Oh, it wasn't that.

'He was chasing a car, when a truck hit him.'

***

Jack the elf went to the doctor. 'I'm so shy Doc I can't even strike up a conversation with the ladies. I'm thirty years old and I have to watch Santa and Emerald having all the luck with the girls.'

'Your problem can be fixed,' said Doctor. 'Simply ring this number and book in for the next course in communication skills.'

A few weeks later, Doc ran into Jack. 'How's your love life, Jack?'

'Incredible, if I decide I want a certain girl I use my communication skills and the next thing I know, I've got her in the cot. 'Thank goodness, I'm no longer the one with a problem, Doc.'

'No, well who is?'

'My fuckin' wife, that's who!'

***

'Doctor you must help me,' Fairy Floss said to her shrink. 'Since I've been working at the hospital I find myself having sex with all the gorgeous young interns. Sometimes I fuck four or five different ones each day, just sex, sex, sex. I feel so depressed and guilty when I go home to my husband.'

'Well, would you like me to give you hypnosis to make you abstain from sex outside the home?'

'Shit no.

'Just give me some hypnosis to prevent me feeling guilty when I go home!'

***

'Ken just isn't interested in sex anymore,' Fairy Floss said to Doctor, 'is there anything he can take to increase his libido?'

'Well yes, I have some wonderful new tablets. Just put one in his food each night and it should help tremendously.'

Fairy Floss was so impressed with Ken's performance after the first tablet she gave him four the next evening. He was hot to trot all night.

On the third evening Fairy Floss thought, 'What the hell,' and tipped all the remaining tablets into his curried prawns.

Next morning, Doctor received a call from Fairy Floss's son. 'Help Doctor, can you come to our house?'

'Is something wrong, Fairyboy?'

'I'll say, I woke up with a sore bum, I think Mommy's dead, my neighbour thinks she's pregnant and Daddy's wandering around.

'He's calling, "Here Kitty, Kitty!"

***

Mrs. Claus was lying flat on her back with her legs in stirrups, waiting for the gynaecologist to begin his examination. As Doctor sat down and pulled his gloves on, he suddenly said, 'My, don't we look pretty today. That's the prettiest one I've seen.'

Mrs. Claus was distressed by Doctor's remarks, she called in on Fairy Floss on her way home. 'I just had to talk to a woman,' she said, 'I think Doctor was most unprofessional.'

'Do you have any idea as to why he mentioned the word pretty?' Fairy Floss asked.

'No. But, I was out of feminine hygiene spray and I did use a kiddie antiperspirant that Fairyboy left at my place.'

'Fairyboy doesn't have an antiperspirant.'

'Well, it had Ken and Barbie on the can and it smelled wonderful.'

'I know what it is,' Fairyboy piped up.

'It's my Ken Doll's golden glitter hair spray!'

***

Santa went to the doctor. 'You've gotta help me Doc, my dick is bright orange.' He dropped his pants.

'Wow you're right, it is bright orange. You must be under a lot of stress, how are things at home?'

'Best they've ever been Doc. Since Mrs. Claus became president of the hospital committee she's always out and I see the Xmas Fairy almost every night, so my sex life is fine.'

'How are things at work?'

'Couldn't be better, we're ahead of schedule.'

'Okay, we have to get to the bottom of this, run me thru your day.'

'Well, Mrs. Claus wakes me each morning. I have a leisurely shower, raid the fridge and wander down to the toy factory. Later I have a nice counter lunch and a few relaxing drinks with the reindeer. I go back to work for awhile until the Xmas Fairy picks me up. We go back to her place and make love. And then we eat and drink.'

'Sounds great, what do you two eat?'

'Well, she's a lousy cook and she hates alcohol.

'We just munch on Jaffas and drink Fanta!'

***

'Ken and I have a sex therapist,' Fairy Floss informed Mrs. Claus, 'and our sex life has improved out of sight.'

'How?'

'Well, she said we should eliminate boredom by trying something new every week. This week she suggested we sit naked on the floor, while Ken tosses grapes at my vagina and I toss donuts at his penis.'

'And?'

'When a grape goes into my pussy Ken has to get it out with his tongue and when a donut lands around his dick, I have to eat it off.'

Mrs. Claus grabbed Santa and rushed to the sex therapist.

The sex therapist explained her technique and after careful consideration she said, 'I'd like you to pick up some "toys" on your way home.'

Mrs. Claus was delighted.

The sex therapist went on.

'I suggest a bag of large apples and a packet of Life Savers!'

***

Mrs. Claus wanted youthful, flawless skin on her face. 'We do skin grafts now,' the plastic surgeon explained. 'I would suggest the skin from your derriere, but we've just used that for your hands. Why don't you ask your husband if we can use the skin off his butt?'

'There's no way Santa would agree.'

'Well, ask him anyway.'

Santa agreed. 'I'd be delighted to give you the skin off my arse Dear, no trouble at all.'

Mrs. Claus was thrilled with her new skin and thrilled with Santa's generosity. 'I can't thank you enough, how can I ever repay you?'

'You already have Dear, many times and you'll probably continue to repay me.'

'But Santa, how?'

'Every time your old bitch of a mother kisses your cheek.

'That's how!'

***

Mrs. Claus consulted her plastic surgeon. 'I want these bags under my eyes removed please Doctor.'

'We have a new technique now,' the surgeon said, 'because bags appear so often, we no longer cut them out. In fact, I'll just put a little crank handle at the back of your head and whenever you notice new bags appearing, you simply crank the little handle and your skin tightens up.'

Mrs. Claus couldn't leave her wondrous crank handle alone, she tightened up on a daily basis. Three months later she complained to the surgeon. 'These latest bags under my eyes wont go Doctor, no matter how hard I crank and they're enormous.'

'They're not bags, they're your boobs.'

'My boobs, are you sure, Doctor?'

'Absolutely.'

'Good grief that probably explains my new goatee beard!'

***

Stupid the elf's wife was in a coma. One day he fondled her right breast as he talked to her, she responded with a faint moan and a slight smile. Stupid fondled her left breast, to see if she would react again.

She did.

He raced out to tell Doctor, 'I suggest you go back in and perform oral sex on your wife and see if she responds, this could be the breakthrough we need.'

Stupid went off to do his duty. He was back in a few minutes. 'Doc quick, she's stopped breathing, I think she's dead.'

'What on earth happened?' Doctor yelled, as he raced to his patient.

'I'm not sure.

'All I know is she moaned for a second and then began to choke!'

***

Fairy Floss arrived at the doctor's surgery. 'You're well advanced with this pregnancy and all looks well,' Doctor announced, 'Is there anything you want to ask?'

'Just one question from Ken, my husband.

'Is it still okay for me to continue as offsider on his garbage truck?'

***

The North Pole doctor hired Mrs. Claus as his receptionist. As Doctor emerged from the Little Boy's room, she happened to notice his fly was undone. Mrs. Claus knew Doctor was ex-Army, so she simply said, 'You forgot to close the door to the barracks.'

Doctor was puzzled until he looked down and realised his zipper was wide open. He decided to give the old girl a thrill.

'When you saw the barracks door standing open Mrs. Claus, did you happen to see a big soldier standing to attention?'

Mrs. Claus saw red.

'Not at all,' she said.

'But I did see a shrivelled up disabled old veteran, sitting on two old, crushed duffle bags!'

***

Santa was having a problem with premature ejaculation. Doctor told him to masturbate just before sex. 'You'll last a lot longer,' he said.

Santa worried about finding some privacy as he needed to do the deed, before he reached the Xmas Fairy's house. He parked the sleigh on the side of the road and crawled underneath. He could pretend to examine the axle.

Just as he was about to blow, someone tapped his bare bum and yelled, 'Police here, what in the hell do you think you're doing?'

'I'm checking out the axle.'

'Well, next time, check your fuckin' brakes first.

'Your sleigh rolled down the hill a few minutes ago!'

***

'Doc, do you know what Viagra and Disneyland have in common?' Santa asked.

'No what?'

'They both make you wait an hour for a two minute ride!'

***

The pharmacist filled Santa's script for Viagra. 'Are these capsules time-release?' Santa asked.

'Sure are.

'They work as soon as your fuckin' cheque clears!'

***

Mrs. Claus asked Santa if he wanted bacon and eggs for breakfast. 'Not really, since I've been taking Viagra my appetite's decreased.'

Later Mrs. Claus said, 'how about I make us a nice salad for lunch while you throw some shrimp on the barbie?'

'Still not hungry, this bloody Viagra stops me from eating.'

Dinnertime dawned and Mrs. Claus was desperate. 'Santa, would you prefer Indian, Chinese or a baked dinner?'

'I keep telling you, Viagra takes my fuckin' appetite away.'

'Well, you'll have to get off me you selfish bastard.

'I'm starving!'

***

'I've got a joke for you Santa,' said Doctor. 'Why did Lancelot come a lot?'

'I'll bite, why?'

'Because he played with his lance a lot!'

****

Ken Floss was playing golf with Santa when a ball hit him in the crown jewels.

'We have to put your dick in a support for a week,' Doctor said. He slapped four tongue depressors around Ken's most treasured possession and tied them firmly together.

'But Doc, I'm off on my honeymoon this week.'

'Tough, you'll just have to put up with it.'

When Ken and Fairy Floss's wedding night arrived, she stepped out of her finery and held her breasts. 'See these,' she said, 'no man has ever seen them before.'

Ken dropped his pants.

'See this?

'It's not even out of the fucken crate!'

***

Fairy Floss complained to her new doctor. 'I'm always tired lately and my energy levels seem low.'

'You might be having too much sex, how many times a week do you have sex?'

'Only Tuesday Thursday and Saturday, why?'

'Well, cut out Saturday for a while and see if it makes a difference.'

'I can't do that.

'Saturday's the night I have sex with my husband!'

***

Mrs. Claus went to the dentist. 'I'm afraid you have a cavity,' he said, 'I'll have to drill.'

'I hope not Doctor I can't stand the pain of a drill, I'd rather have a baby.'

'Well, make up your mind.

'I need to adjust the chair!'

***

'How long will it take to pull my tooth?' Mrs. Claus asked the dentist.

'Oh, should only take about five seconds.'

'And how much will it cost Doctor?'

'$100.'

'That's terribly expensive if you don't mind me saying. That's about $20 per second.'

'Well if it helps, I'll just take a bloody lot longer!'

***

'Your tooth can't be saved, I have to pull it,' the dentist said to Santa, 'so I'll give you a needle to avoid any pain.'

'But, I'm allergic to all dental drugs.' Santa cried.

'Then I'll just have you take two Viagra tablets.'

'How the fuck will Viagra help?'

'Well, you'll need something to hang onto while I pull your tooth!'

***

Ken Floss raced his wife Fairy Floss to the delivery room at the hospital. 'It's going to be a difficult birth,' Doctor said. 'However, I do have a new Pain-Transfer machine. If I connect Fairy Floss to it the pain will transfer from the mother of the child, to the father of the child.'

'Sounds marvellous Doctor, hook me up.'

'Ken, if your pain becomes too intense you must let me know. Okay?'

Fairy Floss was hooked up and the birth commenced. Each time she experienced pain, the machine was turned higher and each time the pain left her.

When the machine reached the maximum of 100 and Ken was still smiling, Doctor marvelled at his high tolerance of pain.

A few days later, Santa drove the happy family home from hospital, he hurried ahead to unlock the front door for the doting parents.

'Look, Fairy Floss,' Santa cried.

'Your mailman's lying dead on the porch!'

***

Santa and Mrs. Claus went to the Marriage Guidance Counsellor. 'How can I help you?' The young professional gushed.

Mrs. Claus folded her arms and rolled her eyes.

'What's his name here, says I don't pay him enough attention.'

***

Santa and Mrs. Claus again visited the pretty, young Marriage Guidance Counsellor. 'I lose my temper so easily lately, with my wife, the elves and the reindeer,' Santa said, 'I've become so disgustingly abusive I need help urgently.'

'Now you just relax Santa and tell me all about it.'

'I just did, you stupid cunt-faced bitch.

'I just did!'

***

The new North Pole doctor took one look at the gorgeous Xmas Fairy and threw the rulebook out the window.

'You have the most beautiful body I have ever seen,' he said as she followed his instructions and began to undress. He fondled her breasts. 'Do you know what I'm doing?'

'Yes Doctor, you're checking for lumps that may lead to breast cancer.'

He moved his hands down and let his fingers wander into her most private parts. 'Do you know what I'm doing?' He asked again.

'Yes Doctor, you're checking for cancer of the cervix.'

Slowly he replaced his fingers with his most cherished possession and began to bonk the Xmas Fairy. 'Now, do you know what I'm doing?' He gasped.

'Yes Doctor, you're catching a mega dose of the crabs.

'That's why I'm here!'

***

Fairy Floss went for her annual check-up. 'I'm too shy to undress in front of you, Doctor,' she said.

'That's okay, I'll just turn the light off and you can let me know when you're ready.'

A few moments later Fairy Floss said, 'I'm undressed Doctor, where shall I put my clothes?'

'Just put them on the chair, next to mine!'

***

Stupid the elf went to the new doctor for a full check up. 'I'll need a urine sample, a blood sample and a sperm sample,' Doctor said.

'No problem Doc'.

'I'll just leave my underpants!'

***

'Santa, your blood pressure is dangerously high,' said Doctor, 'so, no drinking, no gambling, no rich food and no golf until we get it under control.'

'What about sex, I might as well be dead if I can't have sex'

The doctor thought for a moment.

'Well, okay, but only with Mrs. Claus. After all, you mustn't have any excitement at all. How does your wife feel about oral sex?'

'That's a real bugger Doc.

'She thinks oral sex means talking about sex!'

***

A few weeks after Fairy Floss met Ken she asked him to dinner at her parents' home. He stopped off at the pharmacy to stock up on condoms. 'That's quite a supply,' the pharmacist remarked in a disapproving manner.

'And I need quite a supply for the hot little insatiable fox, who's sucking my cock dry and throwing her legs in the air about six times a night.'

As they sat down to dinner, Ken startled Fairy Floss by asking if he could lead the family in giving thanks. Thru out the evening he hogged the conversation and talked on family values; and the sanctity of marriage.

'What the fuck was all that about?' Fairy Floss demanded later. 'When the hell did you become a religious prick?'

'When I realised your father is my friggin' pharmacist.

'That's when!'

***

When Fairy Floss was young and innocent, she spent a year in medical school. At exam time, she was shocked by the first questions.

1. Name the organ of the human body that expands on an almost daily basis to around six times its normal size.

2. Define the conditions under which the organ expands.

Fairy Floss wrote on her exam paper, 'I object to questions of a sexual nature in exams and believe questions 1 and 2 are not relevant to the basics of first year medicine.'

When the exam results came back, a note from the examiner was enclosed. 'Dear Student, Please note the correct answers to questions 1 and 2. They are as follows,

The pupil of the eye.

In dim light.

P.S You have a disgustingly dirty mind and I personally believe you could face extreme disappointment throughout your private life!'

***

It was exam time again at the North Pole School of Medicine and Fairy Floss faced another exam.

Question 1. What common object, enjoyed by male and female humans of heterosexual, homosexual, bi-sexual and paedophilia nature, spends most of its life lying down, waiting for action; has a hole on one end and thick hair on the other end. Is usually six to eight inches long and mostly used to thrust back and forward and in and out of moist warm holes, leaving a pool of sticky, white mush to be cleaned up?

'I know the answer,' Fairy Floss cried.

'Toothbrush!'

Old Timer

Santa's father Old Timer wanted his new young bride to become pregnant. He decided to have a sperm count done. Doctor gave him a specimen cup to take home and fill, with strict instructions to bring it back in the morning.

He arrived back in the morning with an empty cup. 'Why is it empty?' Doctor asked.

'Well, I tried with my right hand and nothing happened, then my left and nothing happened. My wife tried for ages with her mouth and then with both hands and nothing happened. In desperation I asked my son, Santa to try and still nothing happened.

Doctor was shocked. 'You asked your son to try?'

'Sure did.

'And we still couldn't get the fuckin' lid off!'

***

Santa's father rang Doctor's doorbell. 'Come in Old Timer, what can I do for you?'

'Well, I'm married to a very sexy young lady who gives me a blowjob each morning and afternoon. And after she serves me a gourmet meal each evening, she takes me up to bed for a lustful night.' Old Timer began to cry.

'So, what the hell's your problem?'

'I can't remember where I live!'

***

'What can I do for you, Old Timer?' Doctor asked.

'Doc, when I make love to my beautiful young wife my heart pounds, my vision gets bleared and my legs go weak.'

'Well, that's understandable for a man of your years. When did you first notice these symptoms?'

'Let me see now, I noticed them three times last night.

'And three times this morning!'

***

Old Timer had a full check-up. 'Thanks Doc,' he said, 'I'll certainly take your advice.'

A few weeks later, Doc saw him dancing his heart out at a nightclub with a gorgeous young girl in his arms. He looked great. There was no sign of his walking stick and no sign of aches or pains.

'You've improved out of sight,' Doctor said.

'Sure have and I owe it all to you Doc. I took notice when you said, "Get a hot mumma and be cheerful."

'No! I didn't say that.

'I said, "You've got a heart murmur, be careful!"

***

Santa was surprised to see Old Timer waiting in the queue with the children at the shopping centre.

'Santa, will you bring me some Viagra-valium for Xmas please?' Old Timer asked.

'What the hell's Viagra-valium?'

'Well when you don't get a fuck, you don't give a fuck.'

***

Old Timer asked Doctor for the strongest Viagra script available.

'Why the strongest?'

'Cause two young nymphomaniacs are spending the weekend with me.'

Doctor gave him the script. On Monday morning Old Timer was back, he wanted a script for the strongest painkillers available.

'Why, is your dick in agony?' Doctor joked.

'No it's for my hands, Doc.

'The bitches never showed up!'

New Zealand

When Santa delivered his last toy in New Zealand, he looked longingly at the All Night Bar across the road.

'I'd give my balls for a cold beer Rudolph. Do you think anyone would recognise us if I take my hat off and reverse my jacket?'

'Not if we call each other by different names and lie about what we do.'

'Great idea,' said Santa.

So they went inside and had quite a few. When they were finally ordering one for the road, the barman said, 'You guys aren't from around here, where are you from? What do you do?'

Santa looked at the stag's head on the wall. 'We're taxidermists,' he lied, we stuff animals.'

'I was wrong Guys,' the barman called out, "They're one of us".

'They're Kiwis!'

***

While Santa and Rudolph were enjoying a drink in the Kiwi bar, the barman kept up a conversation with a group of locals. Every few minutes he would bellow out above the others, 'Fuck the bastards, fuck the bastards.'

Santa called the barman over.

'Listen Mate if you're gonna talk politics all night, we're leaving!'

***

'Santa, I wonder if they use artificial insemination here in New Zealand?'

'Too right.

'They call it artificial insemination when the farmer does it to the cow!'

***

Why do the reindeer fly so fast over New Zealand?

Because they heard what happens to the sheep.

***

Rudolph had a little lamb.

His case comes up next Tuesday.

***

Santa and Rudolph delivered to a Kiwi dairy. Santa watched a man milk a cow before asking, 'I wonder if you could tell me the time?'

'Sure can, just hold on a minute.' The farmer weighed the cow's udder in his hands and said, 'the time is exactly 8am.'

'Shit,' said Santa, 'I don't believe it.'

Rudolph decided to wait a few minutes and then ask the farmer the same thing. 'I wonder if you can tell me the time please.'

'Sure can,' and once again, the farmer lifted the cow's udder, held it in his hands and said, 'it's exactly 8.10am.'

'How do you do that?'

'Easy, let me show you. Just squat down here cup your hands under the cow's titties and lift them up. Good, now tell me the time.'

'How the fuck can I tell you the time?'

'Just lift them high enough to see the fuckin' clock above the fuckin' barn door!

Psychic

The Xmas Fairy hurried to tell Santa the latest gossip. 'Roberto the contortionist just told me he's marrying a psychic. I wonder what their children will be like.'

Santa thought for a moment.

'Hmmm!

'They'll probably have kids who are capable of seeing their own ends!'

***

Mrs. Claus's time clock was running out, she sent Santa to the fortune teller to ask if they would ever have a family.

'No, you will never be able to father children,' the psychic predicted as she knocked her heavy crystal ball off the table.

It rolled onto Santa's lap.

'And smacked him right in the middle of the crown jewels!

***

The Xmas Fairy was trying to see over her enormous breasts. 'What happened to your breasts?' Mrs. Claus asked.

'I asked the psychic for a boob-increasing spell and for twenty-four hours my boobies grew, whenever anyone said "Pardon me."

'But they're enormous, what went wrong?'

'Well, Abdul stepped on my foot and before I could stop him he yelled, "A thousand pardons, Lovely Lady!"

***

Santa went to the psychic. 'Hitler won't let me deliver toys to the children of Germany. Can you tell me when Hitler will die?'

'Of course, Hitler will die on the Jewish holiday.'

'How can you be so sure?'

'Well any day Hitler dies, will be a Jewish holiday!'

***

Santa went to the bar. He joined Stupid the elf and his two drinking companions, an emu and a cat.

Santa and Stupid each bought a round of drinks. The emu also bought a round of drinks.

The cat passed, he was content to let everyone else pay.

'What's with the cat?' Santa asked.

'The cat's a result of that bloody psychic you sent me to,' Stupid said.

'What happened?'

'Well, I asked her for a spell for a big bird with a tight pussy!'

***

'I don't like that sleazy, new male psychic,' Mrs. Claus complained to the Xmas Fairy, 'he's always drunk. He should be bloody well hung!'

'And he is, he is!' The Xmas Fairy cried.

***

Mrs. Claus grew old and spent her days in a rocking chair. She sent for the psychic. 'I need a spell to make me young forever, a spell to make me rich and a third spell to turn my dear old kitty into a handsome young man, who will adore me forever.'

'No problem,' said the psychic as she cast the first spell and Mrs. Claus became eighteen again.

The psychic cast her second spell and Mrs. Claus's bank book appeared. It showed a balance of billions.

The psychic cast her third spell and her beloved old black cat turned into the most handsome black man in the universe. Mrs. Claus looked into his eyes.

'Go ahead Lover, say something,' she said.

'You're gonna regret having me de-sexed!'

***

The always pissed psychic was upset with his lack of popularity. So he gave himself a reading and predicted he should go to church. The sermon was on the evils of drink.

'Drink is a curse,' the preacher cried, 'the publican is taking all your money. Open your eyes and see his stretch limo, see his mansions, his $5,000 suits and his entourage of scantily dressed young woman.

'Heed my words. The publican is getting rich off you!'

Realisation hit the psychic like a ton of bricks, he packed his bags and left town for a year.

When he returned, it was to present the preacher with a cheque for a million dollars. 'I heard your inspiring sermon and ceased drinking immediately. Today I am rich and successful. Preacher I owe it all to you.'

'Praise the Lord. What business are you in, my son?'

The psychic looked surprised.

'The one you recommended, of course.

'I've become a friggen publican!'

***

The new man in town consulted the North Pole Psychic. 'Because my dick is twenty inches long, women take one look and flee. Can you give me a spell to shorten my dick to eight inches?'

'Certainly, you must go into the forest and face the witch's frog. He sits on a toadstool outside her front door at midnight. You must chant "Abracadabra" three times and ask the frog to marry you. Of course, the frog will say "No." But, every time the frog says "No," your dick will shrink two inches.'

The man found the witch's frog at midnight, performed his chant and asked the frog to marry him. The frog said 'No' and his dick shrank two inches. He repeated the ritual four times, before the frog hopped away.

He went back to the psychic, 'I only lost eight inches and the frog left. I need to lose four more.'

'No problem,' the psychic said, 'go back again and repeat the process. Get the frog to say "No" twice and you'll be right.'

At midnight he found the frog again. He chanted 'Abracadabra' three times and asked the frog to marry him.

'How many fuckin' times do I have to tell you?' The frog yelled.

'No, no, no, no, no!'

***

The Xmas Fairy hurried to the psychic. 'Please Psychic I want my fancy dress costume to be an outstanding success this Xmas. Can you predict a costume to knock everyone's eyes out?'

'Yes but, it won't be comfortable and you will need to rest up for at least a week, after the ball.'

'I'll risk the discomfort just tell me what wear.'

'Okay, first you'll need to get naked then reach back over your head, grab your snatch and pull it up over your head.'

'And?'

'And go as a red backed spider!'

***

Mrs. Clause and Santa sought the psychic's advice on comfortable yet trendy costumes for the fancy dress ball. She handed Mrs. Clause a lemon and told her to go into the bathroom, get naked, and come back with the lemon sticking out of her snatch. Mrs. Claus followed instructions and strutted out. Santa applauded.

'Of course,' he cried, 'she's Sour Puss.'

'Right,' said the psychic as she handed Santa a potato, 'I want you to go to the bathroom, get naked and come back with the potato tied to your dick.'

Santa also followed her instructions. Mrs. Claus and the psychic both applauded loudly.

'I don't get it,' said Santa, 'what the fuck am I?'

'We can't believe you're so dumb,' the ladies cried.

'You're a Dictator!'

Lightning Source UK Ltd.
Milton Keynes UK
UKOW031417141111

182047UK00011B/9/P